C000075874

Basic physical science for technicians

Basic physical science for technicians

A. B. Pollard
BSc, CEng, MIMM, MIM, MICorrT

and

C. W. Schofield
BSc, FIMA, FCSI, FRSH

Edward Arnold

© A. B. Pollard and C. W. Schofield 1977

First published 1977
by Edward Arnold (Publishers) Ltd
25 Hill Street, London W1X 8LL

British Library Cataloguing in Publication Data

Pollard, A B
   Basic physical science for technicians
   1.   Physics
   I.   Title   II. Schofield, Clarence Ward
   530$'$.02$'$46   QC21.2

   ISBN: 0 7131 3384 8

All Rights Reserved. No part of this publication may be reproduced, stored in a retrieval system, or transmitted in any form or by any means, electronic, mechanical, photocopying, recording or otherwise, without the prior permission of Edward Arnold (Publishers) Ltd.

Text set in 10/12 pt IBM Press Roman, printed by photolithography, and bound in Great Britain at The Pitman Press, Bath

Contents

Introduction

In writing this book for technicians studying for certificates and diplomas of the Technician Education Council, we have followed the standard level-1 TEC Physical Science unit. We have tried to cover the objectives of this unit in such a way as to provide a sound basis for subsequent units at other levels. The examples and exercises are drawn from a wide range of possible applications — no student is expected to cover all the material in this volume but a selection should be made appropriate to the particular industry and the corresponding technician course.

A. B. P.
C. W. S.

A   Materials

1 SI units; density

The introduction of SI units (Système International d'Unités) has simplified many calculations, particularly those involving areas, volumes, forces, and masses. SI units have already been adopted by many countries and it is expected that they will replace all other systems of measurement so that eventually units such as the square foot, cubic yard, and pound weight will disappear — no doubt to the relief of future generations of students.

1.1 SI units of length, area, and volume

The SI has seven base units from which a wide range of other quantities may be derived. The basic unit of length is the metre (m), but for the measurement of some lengths the metre is not a suitable unit. To measure the distance from Liverpool to Calcutta or the thickness of a human hair would require very much larger or smaller units. These units are related to the basic unit by the factor 1000.

$$1 \text{ kilometre (km)} = 1000 \text{ metres (m)}$$

$$1 \text{ metre} = 1000 \text{ millimetres (mm)}$$

The SI units of area are derived from SI units of length in the same way as in other systems, that is by multiplying length by width.

Example   What is the area of a room 12 m long and 5.5 m wide?

Area = length x width

= 12 m x 5.5 m

= 66 m^2

The abbreviation m^2 means square metres, and it is important to realize that, although 1 m = 1000 mm, 1 m^2 does not equal 1000 m^2, but

1 m^2 = 1000 mm x 1000 mm = 1 000 000 mm^2

Units of volume are obtained by multiplying length, width, and depth. The cubic metre (m^3) is the basic unit of volume, related to the cubic kilometre by

1

a factor of 10^9 (1000 x 1000 x 1000) and to the cubic millimetre by a factor of 10^{-9} (0.001 x 0.001 x 0.001).

To summarize, the following table may be used:

Length	Area	Volume
metre (m)	square metre (m²)	cubic metre (m³)
kilometre (km)	square kilometre (km²)	cubic kilometre (km³)
millimetre (mm)	square millimetre (mm²)	cubic millimetre (mm³)
$1\,m = 10^3\,mm$	$1\,m^2 = 10^6\,mm^2$	$1\,m^3 = 10^9\,mm^3$
$= 10^{-3}\,km$	$= 10^{-6}\,km^2$	$= 10^{-9}\,km^3$

The three units of length given above will be quite sufficient to cover the sizes of materials in common use, but occasionally very much larger or smaller units will be required. Any SI unit may be made larger or smaller by using prefixes which denote multiplication by a particular amount. The most common of these prefixes are given in the following table:

Prefix	Factor by which the basic unit is multiplied	Symbol
mega	one million, 10^6	M
kilo	one thousand, 10^3	k
centi	one hundredth, 10^{-2}	c
milli	one thousandth, 10^{-3}	m
micro	one millionth, 10^{-6}	μ

In electronics, the prefixes nano (10^{-9}, symbol n) and pico (10^{-12}, symbol p) are also encountered.

These prefixes can be used to produce a range of units of length as follows:

Unit	Equivalent	Symbol
megametre	one million metres, 10^6 m	Mm
kilometre	one thousand metres, 10^3 m	km
centimetre	one hundredth of a metre, 10^{-2} m	cm
millimetre	one thousandth of a metre, 10^{-3} m	mm
micrometre	one millionth of a metre, 10^{-6} m	μm

It is recommended that, where possible, prefixes denoting a multiple of 10^3 should be used, i.e. 10^6, 10^3, 10^{-3}, 10^{-6}, but it is unlikely that the centimetre (10^{-2} m) or the litre (1000 cm³ or 10^{-3} m³) will disappear completely for some time to come.

When using prefixes, the following rules should be followed wherever possible:

i) to avoid cumbersome calculations, use SI units rather than their multiples (e.g. use m x 10^6, not Mm or mm x 10^9);

ii) express quantities with numerical values between 0 and 1000 (e.g. 15 km = 15 x 10^3 m instead of 15 000 m; 5.84 mm = 5.84 x 10^{-3} m instead of 0.005 84 m).

1.2 Mass and weight

The *mass* of a body is defined as *the amount of matter in that body* and is therefore constant. The basic SI unit of mass is the *kilogram* (kg). The standard kilogram is the mass of a certain piece of platinum stored in Paris. For smaller masses the gram (g) is used, and for larger masses the tonne (t) is used. In the laboratory we may need to measure even smaller quantities, and for this purpose we use units of mass as follows:

1 tonne	=	1000 kilograms	=	1 000 000 grams	= 100 000 000 milligrams
1 t	=	10^3 kg	=	10^6 g	= 10^9 mg
		1 kg	=	10^3 g	= 10^6 mg
				1 g	= 10^3 mg

The weight of a body anywhere on the Earth's surface is the force with which the Earth pulls the body to itself. The weight of a body is related to the acceleration due to gravity, which can vary depending on where it is measured and which differs from place to place on the Earth's surface — weight is variable; mass is constant. A device which measures force or weight is the spring balance, but for convenience of everyday use spring balances are usually calibrated in mass units (kilograms), as mass and weight are proportional to each other at any particular place (see section 2). If a quantity of wood screws placed on a spring balance gave a scale reading of 1 unit in London, the same balance and screws would give a reading of 1.002 units if they were moved to the North Pole. If we weighed our screws on the same balance at the Equator, the reading would be 0.996 units. This is because the force of gravity is higher at the Poles than at the Equator.

Weight is really a force acting downwards and it should be measured in terms of the unit of force, which is called the *newton,* after the scientist who explained gravity, Sir Isaac Newton (1642–1727). We will discuss the newton later (section 2.1).

1.3 Density

If a cubic block of wood with all its sides exactly equal to 1 metre were to be compared with similarly sized blocks of steel and sandstone, it would be found that the mass of the block of wood would be one third of that of the stone, which in turn would have a mass of about one third as much as the steel block.

From this it is apparent that the same volumes of different materials do not necessarily contain the same masses of these materials. The property of materials which controls the relationship between mass and volume is known as density: the *density* of a substance may be defined as *its mass divided by its volume*. In the SI system, the density of a substance is defined as *the mass in kilograms contained by 1 cubic metre of the substance (kg/m^3)*. If the masses of the cubes of side 1 metre described above were wood 800 kg, stone 2250 kg, and steel 7800 kg, this would mean that the densities of these materials, in SI units, would be

> wood $0.8 \times 10^3 \, kg/m^3$
>
> sandstone $2.25 \times 10^3 \, kg/m^3$
>
> steel $7.8 \times 10^3 \, kg/m^3$

Densities of some other common substances are given in Table A1.

Material	Density (kg/m^3)	Material	Density (kg/m^3)
Aluminium	2.65×10^3	Cork	0.25×10^3
Copper	8.93×10^3	Rubber	0.95×10^3
Iron	7.87×10^3	Leather	0.9×10^3
Lead	11.37×10^3	Fresh water	1.0×10^3
Flint glass	3.7×10^3	Sea water	1.03×10^3
Crown glass	2.5×10^3	Ice	0.92×10^3
Paraffin	0.8×10^3		

Table A1 Densities of common substances

1.4 Density, mass, and volume of solids

To find the density of a substance we must either take a known mass of the substance and find its volume or take a known volume of the substance and determine its mass.

For a perfectly regular solid, such as a cube, it is easy to measure its dimensions and calculate its volume, but unfortunately most substances whose density is required do not come in such convenient shapes.

In order to find the volume of an irregularly shaped solid or of a powdered material, a method supposed to have been discovered by Archimedes in 300 BC is still in use. He realized that an object will always displace its own volume of water. If you get into a bath filled to the level of the overflow you will cause a volume of water equivalent to your own volume to disappear down the overflow. If an object is immersed in water in a suitable container and the overflow of water is measured, the volume of that object can be determined.

So, a simple method of finding the density of an irregular object is to determine its mass in air and then to lower it into a suitably sized measuring cylinder and note the increase in volume of the contents. For a more accurate determination, the amount of liquid displaced from a container by the substance can be measured and the density of the object can be determined by calculation.

Example 1 An irregular piece of metal has a mass of 6.58 g. When it is immersed in a measuring cylinder with 20 cm^3 of water, the water level rises to 20.95 cm^3. What is the density of the metal?

$$\text{Increase in volume (i.e. water displaced)} = 20.95 \text{ cm}^3 - 20 \text{ cm}^3$$

$$= 0.95 \text{ cm}^3$$

Mass of metal = 6.58 g

$$\text{Density} = \text{mass per unit volume} = \frac{6.58 \text{ g}}{0.95 \text{ cm}^3} = 6.94 \text{ g/cm}^3$$

$$= 6.94 \times 10^3 \text{ kg/m}^3$$

i.e. the density of the metal is 6.94×10^3 kg/m^3.

In order to understand more fully the relationship between the density, mass, and volume of a solid, we will look at several examples.

Example 2 What would be the mass of a 5 m length of 20 mm square-section aluminium rod if the density of aluminium is 2.65×10^3 kg/m^3?

$$\text{Volume of rod} = 5 \text{ m} \times 20 \times 10^{-3} \text{ m} \times 20 \times 10^{-3} \text{ m}$$

$$= 2 \times 10^{-3} \text{ m}^3$$

$$\text{Mass} = \text{volume} \times \text{density}$$

$$= 2 \times 10^{-3} \text{ m}^3 \times 2.65 \times 10^3 \text{ kg/m}^3$$

$$= 5.3 \text{ kg}$$

i.e. the mass is 5.3 kg.

Example 3 What would be the total length of steel rail of rectangular cross-section 25 mm × 60 mm if the mass of the rail were 1 tonne? The density of the steel is 7.8×10^3 kg/m^3.

Let the length of the rail = L metres

$$\text{Volume of rail} = L \text{ m} \times 25 \times 10^{-3} \text{ m} \times 60 \times 10^{-3} \text{ m}$$

$$= L \times 1500 \times 10^{-6} \text{ m}^3$$

$$\text{Volume} = \frac{\text{mass}}{\text{density}}$$

$$= \frac{10^3 \, \text{kg}}{7.8 \times 10^3 \, \text{kg/m}^3} = \frac{1}{7.8} \, \text{m}^3$$

So $\dfrac{1}{7.8} = L \times 1500 \times 10^{-6}$

$$L = \frac{1}{7.8 \times 1500 \times 10^{-6}} = 85.47$$

i.e. the total length of rail is 85.47 m.

Example 4   A piece of metal 350 mm long, 150 mm wide, and 20 mm thick has a mass of 10.5 kg. What is its density?

$$\text{Volume of metal} = 350 \, \text{mm} \times 150 \, \text{mm} \times 20 \, \text{mm}$$

$$= 1.05 \times 10^6 \, \text{mm}^3$$

$$= 1.05 \times 10^{-3} \, \text{m}^3$$

$$\text{Density} = \frac{\text{mass}}{\text{volume}}$$

$$= \frac{10.5 \, \text{kg}}{1.05 \times 10^{-3} \, \text{m}^3} = 10^4 \, \text{kg/m}^3$$

i.e. the density of the metal is $10^4 \, \text{kg/m}^3$.

Example 5   Arrange the following 50 mm x 50 mm square bars of different lengths in order of increasing mass, using the values of density from section 1.3: (a) steel, 2 m long; (b) wood, 15 m long; (c) copper, 1.8 m long; (d) aluminium, 8 m long.

a) Volume of steel $= 2 \, \text{m} \times 50 \times 10^{-3} \, \text{m} \times 50 \times 10^{-3} \, \text{m}$

$$= 5 \times 10^{-3} \, \text{m}^3$$

Mass = volume x density

Mass of steel $= 5 \times 10^{-3} \, \text{m}^3 \times 7.8 \times 10^3 \, \text{kg/m}^3$

$$= 39 \, \text{kg}$$

b) Volume of wood $= 15 \, \text{m} \times 50 \times 10^{-3} \, \text{m} \times 50 \times 10^{-3} \, \text{m}$

$$= 37.5 \times 10^{-3} \, \text{m}^3$$

Mass = volume x density

$$\text{Mass of wood} = 37.5 \times 10^{-3} \, m^3 \times 0.8 \times 10^3 \, kg/m^3$$

$$= 27.9 \, kg$$

c) $\text{Volume of copper} = 1.8 \, m \times 50 \times 10^{-3} \, m \times 50 \times 10^{-3} \, m$

$$= 4.5 \times 10^{-3} \, m^3$$

$\text{Mass} = \text{volume} \times \text{density}$

$\text{Mass of copper} = 4.5 \times 10^{-3} \, m^3 \times 8.93 \times 10^3 \, kg/m^3$

$$= 40.185 \, kg$$

d) $\text{Volume of aluminium} = 8 \, m \times 50 \times 10^{-3} \, m \times 50 \times 10^{-3} \, m$

$$= 20 \times 10^{-3} \, m^3$$

$\text{Mass} = \text{volume} \times \text{density}$

$\text{Mass of aluminium} = 20 \times 10^{-3} \, m^3 \times 2.65 \times 10^3 \, kg/m^3$

$$= 53 \, kg$$

i.e. the wood is the lightest, followed by the steel, copper, and aluminium.

1.5 Density of liquids

The method described in section 1.4 is suitable for finding the density of all solids with a density greater than that of water, but another method is needed to cope with liquids whose density needs to be known. Again, volume and mass need to be measured.

The simplest method for a rapid determination is to run out a measured quantity of the liquid into a container and determine its mass; then divide the mass by the volume. For more accurate determinations a density bottle is used. This is a flat-bottomed glass bottle with a ground-glass stopper which has a small hole through it (fig. A1). The volume of the bottle may be determined by measuring the mass of water it will hold at around $4°C$, as at this temperature $1 \, cm^3$ of water has a mass of 1 g. The reason for the hole through the stopper will be clear if the bottle is filled to the brim. When the stopper is replaced, excess liquid overflows through this hole and, if the sides of the bottle are wiped dry, exactly the same volume of liquid will be held in the bottle each time it is filled.

The method of determining the density of a liquid is as follows. Use a balance to determine the mass of a clean, dry bottle. Fill it with the given liquid, avoiding the presence of air bubbles. Insert the stopper. Dry the bottle and use the balance again. Pour the liquid back into its container, wash the bottle thoroughly, and fill it with water. Again insert the stopper, dry the outside of the bottle, and replace on the balance. From the balance readings the density of the liquid may be determined. A typical set of results is given below:

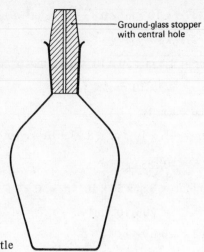

Ground-glass stopper
with central hole

Fig. A1 Density bottle

Mass of bottle filled with liquid	153.85 g	(i)
Mass of bottle	98.25 g	(ii)
Mass of liquid	55.60 g	(i)−(ii)
Mass of bottle filled with water	169.50 g	(iii)
Mass of water	71.25 g	(iii)−(ii)
Volume of water (1 cm³ ≡ 1 g)	71.25 cm³	

$$\text{Density of liquid} = \frac{\text{mass}}{\text{volume}} = \frac{55.60}{71.25} = 0.78 \text{ g/cm}^3$$

$$= 0.78 \times 10^3 \text{ kg/m}^3$$

1.6 Relative density

In section 1.3 we considered blocks of wood, steel, and sandstone — all of the same size — and said that the mass of the block of wood would be about one third that of the stone, which in turn would have a mass of about one third as much as the steel block. From the masses of the blocks, we said that the densities of these substances were

wood $0.8 \times 10^3 \text{ kg/m}^3$
sandstone $2.25 \times 10^3 \text{ kg/m}^3$
steel $7.8 \times 10^3 \text{ kg/m}^3$

Thus, the density of wood is about one third the density of sandstone which in turn is about one third the density of steel, i.e. the density of any one of these substances can be expressed in terms of the density of any other one.

8

This idea is used in defining a quantity known as *relative density*, which expresses the density of a substance in terms of the density of water: the relative density of a substance is *the ratio of the density of that substance to the density of water* or *the ratio of the mass of a given volume of the substance to the mass of the same volume of water.*

$$\text{Relative density} = \frac{\text{density of substance}}{\text{density of water}}$$

$$= \frac{\text{mass of substance}}{\text{mass of same volume of water}}$$

Note that the relative density will be a number, without units, as it is a ratio of densities.

Taking the density of water as 10^3 kg/m^3, we can see that the relative densities of wood, sandstone, and steel are 0.8, 2.25, and 7.8 respectively.

Exercise A1

1. (a) Calculate the area in square metres of a corridor 6500 mm long and 1400 mm wide.
   (b) What are the lengths of the sides of a square courtyard in metres if its area is 981 m^2?

2. Calculate the mass of a brick partition wall 2.5 m high, 4 m long, and 0.25 m thick if the density of the brickwork is $1.5 \times 10^3 \text{ kg/m}^3$.

3. (a) What is the height of a room with sides 3.6 m and 5.0 m if its volume is 36 m^3?
   (b) How many litres of paint would it take to cover the two larger sides and the ceiling if 1 litre of paint would cover 15 m^2?

4. (a) A block of wood is 600 mm x 150 mm x 60 mm and it has a mass of 4.8 kg. Calculate its density.
   (b) If a piece of aluminium of exactly the same size were to replace the wood, what would be its mass?

5. What would be the total mass of a wooden structure composed of 10 m of 10 cm x 2 cm timber, 5 m of 5 cm x 5 cm timber, and 5 m of 20 cm x 2 cm timber? (Density of timber = 800 kg/m^3.)

6. Which of the following would be the longest: a rectangular-section copper bar 20 mm x 30 mm of mass 15 kg, a square aluminium bar 60 mm x 60 mm of mass 10 kg, or a rectangular steel bar 25 mm x 40 mm of mass 20 kg?

7. The following results were obtained by using a gravity bottle to determine the density of an unknown liquid. Calculate the density of the liquid.

Mass of the bottle filled with liquid	165.25 g
Mass of bottle	110.15 g
Mass of bottle filled with water	182.20 g

9

2 Effects of forces on materials

2.1 Force

In Chapter 1 we mentioned that the weight of an object is a measure of the force with which the object is attracted, or pulled, towards the Earth. A force is any push or pull, and it can have a number of effects on a body:

a) it can make a body at rest start to move, or it can make a body which is already moving travel faster or slower or in a different direction, depending on the direction in which the force acts — i.e. it accelerates the body;
b) it can change the shape of the body; or
c) it can be exactly resisted by other forces and have no obvious effect on the body

As a force always *tries* to change the way in which a body is moving, *force* can be defined as *that which changes or tends to change the motion of a body*.

The ability of a force to produce acceleration is used to define the *newton*, (abbreviation N), which is the unit used to measure forces. A force of *one newton is the force which will give a mass of 1 kg an acceleration of 1 m/s²*, assuming that the mass is free to move. From this definition we can calculate forces by using the equation

force = mass x acceleration

We can find the weight of a body by letting the acceleration in this equation be the acceleration due to gravity. As we said in section 1.2, this varies from place to place on the Earth; however for most purposes we can assume that the acceleration due to gravity is 9.81 m/s² and we then have

weight of body = mass of body x acceleration due to gravity

or, in SI units,

weight (N) = mass (kg) x 9.81 (m/s²)

We shall talk about acceleration in general terms in section 14.6 and we shall need to make use of these equations to calculate weight in section 4, but in the following sections we are going to discuss what happens when a force acts on a body that is not free to move and the way in which the material from which the body is made influences this.

Different forces

The three main types of force that can act on a body are

a) tension,
b) compression,
c) shear.

When a pull is exerted on a rope attached to a heavy object, the rope is subject to a force which attempts to stretch it. This force is called *tension* and it acts in the direction of the pull.

If a locomotive pushes a railway wagon up an incline, the buffers on the wagon and the locomotive are subjected to a force which attempts to push them closer together. This force acts in the direction of the push and is called *compression*. It acts in the opposite direction to tension.

One example of the third type of force which is commonly encountered in engineering applications occurs when a guillotine blade presses down on a sheet of metal and causes it to part along a plane which is in the direction of the force. This type of force is called a *shear* force. Figure A2 shows examples of tension, compression, and shear forces.

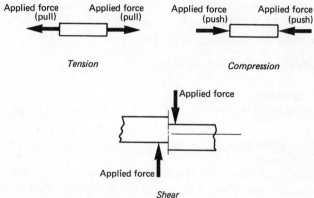

Fig. A2 Types of force

2.2 Elasticity
When subject to a load which may produce tension, compression, or shear, most engineering materials will distort but will return to their original dimensions when the load is removed. This property of returning to the original shape and size after a load has been removed is called *elasticity*.

2.3 Hooke's law
In 1676, Robert Hooke (1635–1703) published his law which states that *for an elastic material, the strain is proportional to the stress.*

Before the significance of this may be appreciated, we must define strain and stress. If a wire or a rod is loaded at one end, it stretches and the *strain* may be defined as *the amount by which the body stretches, expressed as a fraction of its original length.* So, if a rod of original length 1 m is subject to a load which causes it to stretch by 2 mm,

11

$$\text{strain} = \frac{\text{extension}}{\text{original length}}$$

$$= \frac{2 \times 10^{-3} \, m}{1 \, m} = 0.002$$

Strain is a ratio and is a number without units, but both extension and original length must be expressed in the same units. The *stress* is defined as *the force acting on the material per unit cross-sectional area.* So, if a rod of cross-sectional area 100 mm² has a pull of 5 kN exerted on it, the stress is given by

$$\text{stress} = \frac{5 \times 10^3 \, N}{100 \times 10^{-6} \, m^2} = 5 \times 10^7 \, N/m^2$$

The SI unit of stress is the newton per square metre — this is sometimes referred to as the pascal (Pa) to honour the French physicist and philosopher Blaise Pascal (1623–62). Frequently it is more convenient to use N/mm² as a measure of stress in engineering applications:

$$1 \, N/mm^2 = 1 \, MN/m^2 = 10^6 \, N/m^2$$

2.4 Problems involving Hooke's law

It follows from Hooke's Law that, if the strain is proportional to the stress, then

$$\frac{\text{stress}}{\text{strain}} = \text{constant}$$

This constant, usually designated by E, is called the *modulus of elasticity* or *Young's modulus*, after Thomas Young (1773–1829) who, when he was not investigating the elastic properties of materials, was the first man to translate the Egyptian hieroglyphics on the Rosetta stone at the British Museum.

So, if we know E for a material and we are given the force acting on a material and its cross-sectional area, we can calculate the change in length that will be produced by this force.

Example 1 A steel rod 5 m long and with a diameter of 40 mm is stretched by a load of 100 kN. Calculate the extension if $E = 200\,000 \, MN/m^2$.

$$\text{Area of cross-section of rod} = \pi \times 20^2 = 1256 \, mm^2$$

$$= 1256 \times 10^{-6} \, m^2$$

$$\text{Load} = 100 \times 10^3 \, N$$

$$\text{Stress} = \frac{\text{load}}{\text{cross-sectional area}} = \frac{100 \times 10^3 \, N}{1256 \times 10^6 \, m^2}$$

$$E = \frac{\text{stress}}{\text{strain}} = 200\,000 \, MN/m^2 = 200 \times 10^9 \, N/m^2$$

12

$$\text{strain} = \frac{\text{stress}}{E} = \frac{100 \times 10^3}{1256 \times 10^{-6} \times 200 \times 10^9}$$

$$= 3.98 \times 10^{-4}$$

$$\text{Strain} = \frac{\text{extension}}{\text{original length}}$$

$$\text{extension} = \text{strain} \times \text{original length}$$

$$= 3.98 \times 10^{-4} \times 5 \text{ m}$$

$$= 19.90 \times 10^{-4} \text{ m}$$

$$= 1.99 \text{ mm}$$

i.e. the extension is 1.99 mm.

Example 2 Young's modulus for an aluminium alloy is 75×10^9 N/m². Calculate the maximum pull that can be applied to a 1 m rod made of this material if it must not extend by more than 2 mm. The cross-sectional area of the rod is 200 mm².

$$\text{Maximum allowable strain} = \frac{\text{extension}}{\text{original length}}$$

$$= \frac{2 \times 10^{-3} \text{ m}}{1 \text{ m}} = 2 \times 10^{-3}$$

If $E = 75 \times 10^9$ N/m²,

$$\frac{\text{maximum stress}}{\text{maximum strain}} = E$$

$$\frac{\text{stress}}{2 \times 10^{-3}} = 75 \times 10^9 \text{ N/m}^2$$

$$\text{stress} = 2 \times 10^{-3} \times 75 \times 10^9 \text{ N/m}^2$$

$$= 150 \times 10^6 \text{ N/m}^2$$

$$\text{Stress} = \frac{\text{load}}{\text{cross-sectional area}}$$

$$\text{load} = \text{stress} \times \text{cross-sectional area}$$

$$= 150 \times 10^6 \text{ N/m}^2 \times 200 \times 10^{-6} \text{ m}^2$$

$$= 3 \times 10^4 \text{ N}$$

$$= 30 \text{ kN}$$

i.e. the maximum allowable pull is 30 kN.

2.5 Brittle and ductile materials

If a wire is subjected to a tensile test in which it is stretched by applying to it a gradually increasing force, the following results are typical of those that might be obtained if the wire is made of steel. For each value of load that is taken, the length of the specimen under test is measured.

Load (N)	0	20	40	60	80	90	100	105	110	120	130	145	150
Extension (mm)	0	0.22	0.50	0.75	2.1	4.0	7.5	10.4	13.0	18.6	26.0	43.0	55.0

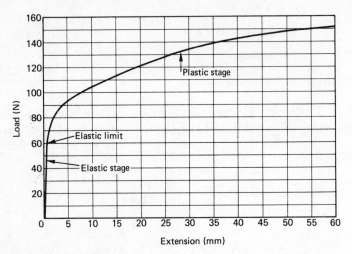

Fig. A3 Extension of a wire

If the results are plotted on a graph, fig. A3 results. This shows two distinct regions. Up to a load of about 60 N the extension is small and proportional to the load, so a straight line results. During this stage of the test it would be found that, if the load were removed, the wire would return to its original length. We call this the *elastic* stage. At loads above this value, the extension caused by a given increase in load is much greater than at loads below 60 N. If the load were removed at this stage, the wire would remain stretched. This stage is said to be the *plastic* stage, and the material is said to be showing *ductility*. Ductility may be defined as *the ability to be permanently stretched without fracturing.*

For a ductile material such as mild steel, this plastic stage can be quite long and considerable extensions can result. However, for a *brittle* material, such as heavily cold-worked steel, the elastic stage would be followed by immediate fracture with virtually no plastic stage.

Another property of materials which is important in many engineering applications is *malleability* or *the ability to be permanently compressed without fracture.*

14

Exercise A2

1. Calculate the stress in a rod of cross-sectional area 300 mm² under a load of 980 N.
2. Calculate the load that produces a stress of 750 kN/m² in a square-section rod of side 2 mm.
3. What is the maximum pull that can be withstood by a tie-rod of cross-sectional area 2 000 mm² if the stress is limited to 150 MN/m²?
4. A metal rod of cross-sectional area 75 mm² and 1 m long is stretched 6 mm by a pull of 9 kN. Calculate the value of E for the material.
5. A metal rod, cross-sectional area 80 mm², is subjected to a pull of 40 kN. Calculate (a) the stress, (b) the strain, and (c) the extension on a length of 500 mm. E for the metal = 150 000 MN/m².
6. Calculate the cross-sectional area of a metal rod which has to carry a load of 10 kN if the maximum allowable extension is 5 mm on a length of 1 m. E = 200 000 N/mm².
7. A mass of 1 tonne is hung on the end of a steel cable 10 m long and cross-sectional area 500 mm². If E for the steel is 250 000 N/mm², calculate (a) the stress in the cable and (b) the extension.
8. What is the maximum pull that can be applied to a 50 m long copper wire of cross-sectional area 80 mm² with a Young's modulus of 110 000 N/mm² if the wire must not extend by more than 10 cm?

3 Atomic structure of matter and its crystalline forms

In this section we shall see that all substances, including those that appear solid and dense, are in fact made up of very much smaller component parts which are in the majority of cases arranged in a regular pattern.

3.1 Atoms and molecules

The idea that all substances are composed of very large numbers of very small particles is not new — Leucippus (500 BC) and Democritus (450 BC) were two early investigators who held this view. In 1803, John Dalton realized the significance of their ideas and put forward the idea that a small indivisible particle, *the atom* (from the Greek *atomos*, meaning indivisible), existed and that millions of these particles went to make up a mass of any substance. For a long time it was thought that the atom could not be altered or destroyed, but with modern nuclear physics it has been realized that the atom itself is composed of much smaller particles such as electrons, protons, and neutrons, and under certain circumstances an atom may be divided or modified.

The atom is the smallest part of a substance that can enter into, or be expelled from, chemical combination. This means that certain properties of a material are derived from the basic properties of its atoms, but there are other properties that are derived from the way that the atoms are arranged with respect to each other.

In order to understand the reasons for most of the engineering properties of a substance, it is not necessary for us to have a detailed picture of the structure of the atom, and the idea of the atom as a small, virtually indivisible particle having a definite relationship with its fellow atoms is quite adequate.

The mass of the atom in grams is very small (2.64×10^{-23} g for the oxygen atom) so masses of atoms are usually calculated on a scale where carbon is given a value of 12. On this scale the mass of the atom is called its *relative atomic mass.* Relative atomic masses of some common elements are given in Table A2.

Hydrogen	1	Zinc	65
Carbon	12	Silver	108
Aluminium	27	Tin	119
Iron	56	Gold	197
Nickel	59	Lead	207
Copper	63		

Table A2 Relative atomic masses of some common elements

We have already seen that the atom is the smallest particle that can enter into chemical combination. However, there are large numbers of substances such as copper sulphate, common salt, and sugar which contain atoms of more than one sort. Copper sulphate is made up of copper, sulphur, and oxygen atoms; common salt is made up of sodium and chlorine atoms; sugar is made up of carbon, hydrogen, and oxygen atoms, all in certain definite proportions.

If one particle of any of these substances is tested in any way, it will be found to have exactly the same properties as the bulk of the material, however small it is. If the particle is crushed and reduced in size, its properties will still remain the same. If it were possible to carry on this reduction in size indefinitely, the stage would be reached, in the case of common salt, where a particle containing one sodium atom and one chlorine atom remained. The smallest part of a substance which can have exactly the same properties as the substance is known as a *molecule.* All molecules of the same substance are identical, so every molecule of salt contains one sodium and one chlorine atom (NaCl).

In a chemical change, the molecules present are altered. If a piece of clean iron (Fe) is put into copper-sulphate solution, iron sulphate is formed and copper metal precipitates from the solution. This is represented by the equation

$$CuSO_4 + Fe = Cu + FeSO_4$$

copper sulphate + iron = copper + iron sulphate

The molecules have altered but the atoms remain exactly the same.

16

Some pure substances, particularly gases like oxygen and chlorine, tend to exist not as separate atoms but as molecules which contain two atoms of the gas combined together. This is why oxygen is usually written as O_2 in chemical equations.

3.2 The structure of atoms and molecules

The simplest picture of the structure of an atom is that of a small solar system with a central portion, the nucleus, around which, at a large distance relative to the size of the nucleus, move very much smaller particles in certain fixed bands. The nucleus consists of particles of no electrical charge called *neutrons* and particles with a positive charge called *protons*. The particles rotating around the nucleus are called *electrons* and are negatively charged. In an atom, the number of negative particles exactly balances the number of positive particles (protons). It is the number of protons that controls the properties of the atom. The lightest element, hydrogen, has one proton in its nucleus; the next lightest, helium, has two protons. The number of protons in an atom is called its *atomic number*. The atomic numbers of the elements given in the preceding section are given in Table A3.

Hydrogen	1	Zinc	30
Carbon	6	Silver	47
Aluminium	13	Tin	50
Iron	26	Gold	79
Nickel	28	Lead	82
Copper	29		

Table A3 Atomic numbers of some common elements

Until comparatively recently it was accepted that the highest possible number of protons that could be accommodated in the nucleus of an atom was 92 — which occurred in the radioactive element uranium — but modern methods have detected elements with over 100 protons in their nuclei.

Molecules, as already mentioned, are composed of more than one atom in a stable fixed composition. A discussion of the forces that keep the atoms in a molecule together is outside the scope of this work, but it is necessary to realize that these forces can vary between different types of molecule. For example, the forces that hold the two oxygen atoms together in the oxygen molecule are different from those that keep together sodium and chlorine atoms in sodium chloride. At this stage it is sufficient to realize that the outermost electrons are the key factors in the bonds that keep atoms together.

3.3 Elements, compounds, and mixtures

The matter which constitutes the universe falls into three separate classes — elements, compounds, and mixtures. An *element* is *the simplest form of matter*

17

and cannot be changed into simpler substances by normal chemical means.
Typical elements are iron, copper, oxygen, nitrogen, carbon, gold, and
aluminium. A sample of an element, however prepared and from any source,
will always contain atoms of only one type.

If iron filings are shaken in a stoppered bottle containing oxygen, the composition of the contents of the bottle can vary depending on how big the bottle
is and on how many iron filings are in the bottle. This combination of iron
atoms and oxygen molecules is called a mixture and its composition is not fixed
in any definite way.

> *A mixture can contain two or more substances in any proportion.*

Examples of mixtures encountered in engineering include the solders, which
can have varying amounts of lead and tin depending on their uses; brasses, which
contain copper and zinc in different amounts; bronzes, which are mixtures of
copper, tin, and certain other metals; and welding and cutting gases which are
mixtures of air or oxygen and combustibles such as acetylene, propane, or
butane.

Returning to our mixture of iron filings and oxygen in a stoppered bottle, if
this is heated sufficiently a definite change will occur on cooling the residue.
The solid, which was previously strongly magnetic, would now show less magnetism and its melting point would have changed from 1535 °C to about 1650 °C.
This is because the iron atoms and oxygen molecules in the mixture have combined to form a *compound.*

> *A compound always contains the same elements combined in the same
> fixed proportions.*

In this case, the compound is magnetite (Fe_3O_4), which, however it is manufactured, always contains 26.2% oxygen by weight.

The reaction that has occurred is as follows:

$$3Fe + 2O_2 = Fe_3O_4$$

3 iron atoms + 2 oxygen molecules = 1 magnetite (iron oxide) molecule

Magnetite is a compound. Other examples already mentioned include common salt (sodium chloride, NaCl), which is a compound of sodium and chlorine,
and copper sulphate ($CuSO_4$), which contains one atom of copper, one of
sulphur, and four of oxygen. Iron carbide (cementite, Fe_3C), the hard con-
stituent of plain-carbon steels, is another common compound, containing three
iron atoms and one carbon atom.

Chemical equations
In the preceding sections we have used chemical equations which show reactions
between molecules and/or atoms,

e.g. $3Fe + 2O_2 = Fe_3O_4$

These chemical equations are similar to mathematical equations in that they have to balance exactly. If we consider the above example, on both sides there are three atoms of iron and four of oxygen; on the left-hand side they are arranged as three atoms of iron and two molecules of oxygen, on the right-hand side as one molecule of magnetite (iron oxide).

If we examine this equation, it can be seen that all it shows is that the atoms are rearranged as a result of the reaction and no net change in the number of atoms occurs.

Exercise A3

1. Explain the difference between elements, compounds, and mixtures.
2. Group the following under the three headings 'elements', 'compounds', and 'mixtures': cast iron, town gas, methane, hydrogen, copper, zinc, brass, silica, sea water, ice, graphite, lead, concrete, distilled water.
3. What is the difference between an atom and a molecule? Give five examples of each.
4. What is the difference between 'atomic number' and 'relative atomic mass'?
5. An oxygen atom has a mass of 2.64×10^{-23} g. Calculate the number of atoms in 1 gram of copper.

3.4 Solutions

We have already seen the differences between pure substances, mixtures, and compounds. There is however a particular kind of mixture which has special properties and is encountered more frequently than any other type of mixture.

A common example of this type of mixture is the ordinary morning cup of tea. Depending on your own taste you add sugar to the hot liquid and, provided that you stir the tea and that you are not excessively extravagant with the sugar, it all dissolves in the tea. The sugar does not change into something else; it remains as sugar which can be identified by its sweet taste, even though you can no longer see it. The more sugar you add to the tea, the sweeter it tastes. The other obvious property of the sugar is that it is uniformly spread through the tea. Provided that the tea has been stirred, the first mouthful tastes as sweet as the last. Obviously the sugar has entered the tea, but how?

In fact, what has happened is that a *solution* has been formed by the sugar dissolving in the tea.

A solution is a special kind of mixture in which the molecules of its components have a special relationship with each other. The names given to the various components of the solution are as follows. The liquid which provides the bulk of the solution and in which the solid dissolves (in this case the cup of tea) is called the *solvent;* the solid which dissolves (i.e. the sugar) is called the *solute.*

A solution is a mixture from which the two constituents may not be separated either by the action of gravity or by any form of filtration.

So, sweet tea poured through a filter comes out as sweet tea the other side.

3.5 Suspensions

Sand does not dissolve in water, so if you add sand to water you cannot make a sand solution. When you stir some sand into water, for a short time the sand is uniformly distributed throughout the water, but as particles that are considerably larger than single molecules. After a relatively short time, most of the sand falls to the bottom of the container. If some of the particles of sand are very fine they can remain dispersed in the water, but pouring the water through a filter will remove the sand. If we compare this with the solution we can see that this type of mixture has different properties — it is called a *suspension.*

A suspension consists of particles of solid, each one containing many molecules, surrounded by liquid. The solid may be separated from the liquid by gravity or by filtration.

Solution and suspension are not restricted to a solid in a liquid. Most gases will dissolve in liquids and in some cases in solids, and many liquids dissolve in other liquids. Fine solids and liquid droplets will also occur as suspensions in gases, a common example being the spray from an aerosol. Solids will also dissolve in solids — alloys, which are mixtures of metals, may contain solid solutions (see section 3.12).

3.6 Solubility

The property of being able to dissolve in another substance is called *solubility*. In order to examine this property in more detail, we can look at what happens when potassium dichromate, which is a bright orange chemical, is added to water. If water at 15 °C is used, and is kept well stirred as the potassium dichromate is added, the orange particles will disappear and the water will take on a characteristic orange colour. If exactly 100 grams of water are used in this experiment, it will be found that at 15 °C it will be possible to make 9.6 g of chemical dissolve in them. Any more than 9.6 g will remain undissolved in the solvent. So we can say that at 15 °C the solubility of potassium dichromate in water is 9.6 grams.

If the temperature of the water is then raised to 30 °C, a further 8.5 g of potassium dichromate will dissolve, so the solubility of potassium dichromate in water at 30 °C is 18.1 grams.

In general, *the solubility of a substance is the maximum amount of that substance, in grams, which will dissolve in 100 grams of a particular solvent at a given temperature.* Note that the solvent and the temperature must be stated.

3.7 Factors influencing solubility

For most materials, the solubility, or the amount of a solute that will dissolve in a particular solvent, is dependent on temperature. As a general rule for solids dissolving in liquids, as the temperature increases so does the amount of solid that will go into solution. There are one or two exceptions — the solubility of sodium chloride in water remains almost constant, and the solubility of calcium hydroxide actually decreases as the temperature rises.

Figure A4 shows how the solubilities of some common chemical salts change with temperature.

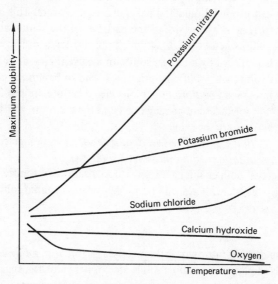

Fig. A4 The change in maximum solubility with increase in temperature

With gases dissolved in liquids, as a general rule, the solubility decreases as the temperature rises. This decrease can be observed by watching tap water being heated. As the temperature rises, the air dissolved in the tap water starts to bubble out as its solubility becomes less.

There are other factors that affect the solubility of solids in liquids. We know that 100 grams of water at 15 °C will dissolve 9.6 grams of potassium dichromate. If two identical containers each contain 100 grams of water at 15 °C and into one is placed 9.6 grams of finely crushed potassium dichromate and into the other one or two very large lumps of potassium dichromate, again with a mass of 9.6 grams, the finely divided chemical will dissolve first. The reason for this is that solution of a solid in a liquid takes place at the surface between the solid and the liquid as the molecules of solid detach themselves from the bulk of the solid and enter the liquid. With a surface effect of this type, it is apparent that, the larger the surface area, the more rapid is the rate of solution — the maximum solubility is attained earlier with finer particles because there is a larger area of surface in contact with the liquid.

When a soluble solid is added to a container with water in it, the solid dissolves more rapidly if the water is stirred. This is not because its solubility in water is affected but because the solvent which has just dissolved some of the solid is replaced by a fresh supply of solvent when the liquid is stirred.

3.8 Saturated solutions

We have already seen (section 3.6) that there is a certain maximum amount of solid which will dissolve in a liquid at a particular temperature. This quantity is not affected by stirring or by the size of the particles of the solute, although these two factors will control the rate at which the substance dissolves.

If a solution is prepared by adding a solute to a solvent and, after prolonged stirring, no more solute will go into solution, it is said to be *saturated*. A state occurs which is known as *equilibrium* — molecules of solute are passing into solution, dissolved molecules are passing out from the solution, and the rates of both of these reactions are the same.

A saturated solution can then be described as *a solution, at a given temperature, which is in equilibrium with undissolved solid.*

Thus, if a piece of copper sulphate is placed in a saturated solution, no apparent change will occur. If placed in a weaker or *unsaturated* solution it will dissolve.

3.9 Crystals

All solids can be divided into two distinct classes: *crystalline solids* and *amorphous solids*. Examples of crystalline solids are copper sulphate, sugar, salt, and ice. They are so called because they exist as crystals. Substances which do not exist as crystals, such as glass, wood, and pitch, are called *amorphous* substances. There are several properties that crystalline solids possess that distinguish them from amorphous solids. The most easily detectable property is to do with their form and consequently their appearance. *Crystals are always bounded by flat faces which intersect one another at definite angles*. These angles, and the angles between the edges of the faces, are fixed within very narrow limits and normally have values that are simple fractions of $360°$ (e.g. $45°$, $60°$, $90°$) — figs A5 to A8 show some examples. Even though different faces of a crystal may not be developed equally, giving rise to an irregularly shaped crystal, the angles at which the faces and edges meet are the same in all crystals of the solid. In fig. A7, which shows an irregular crystal of sodium chloride, all the faces and edges still meet at $90°$.

In fig. A8 you can see a cross-section of a series of crystals of beryllium aluminum silicate ($Al_2Be_3Si_6O_{18}$) — this is the correct chemical name for the green precious stone normally known as emerald. It can be seen that there are

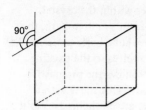

Fig. A5 Common salt (sodium chloride) crystal

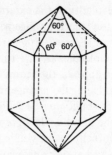

Fig. A6 Quartz (silica) crystal

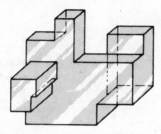

Fig. A7 Irregular crystal of common salt (sodium chloride)

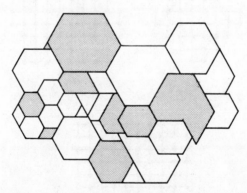

Fig. A8 Cross-section of crystals of beryllium aluminium silicate (emerald)

some perfect hexagonal crystals, some irregular hexagons, some four-sided crystals, and some triangles. However, the basic structure is such that all the faces meet at either 120° or 60°, the characteristic angles of the hexagon.

23

This regularity in the external form of a crystal, or the 'habit' as it is called, is due to the regular arrangement of atoms or molecules within the crystal. When a crystal grows, either from a liquid solution or from a molten bath, the atoms or molecules arrange themselves in one of a few regular basic patterns. As more solid appears, the atoms or molecules attach themselves to the existing pattern and a regular arrangement builds up. Figure A9 shows the progressive stages in the build-up of a solid that has a cubic structure. This starts with a simple cube of solid which, as more atoms or molecules attach themselves to it, grows eventually into a visible regular crystal. However, crystal growth does not normally start at one single point in a liquid — it can occur at many thousand different sites or *nuclei*. As more and more solid appears, the crystals may inter-fere with each other's growth, and irregularities can occur. These irregularities do not, however, destroy the basic angles of the cube.

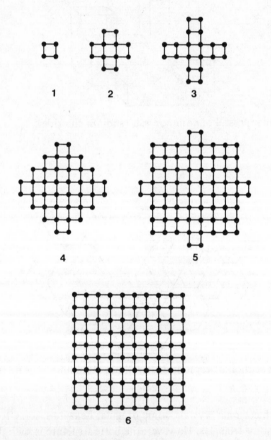

Fig. A9 Stages in the growth of a cubic crystal

24

The importance of the regularity of the arrangement of the atoms or molecules within the crystal will be understood later. All we need to appreciate at this stage is that within each individual crystal is a near-perfect, regular arrangement of atoms or molecules stretching in all directions. The assumption that the arrangement continues regularly throughout the crystal can be more easily accepted if it is realized that within a cubic crystal of sodium chloride of 1 mm side there are no less than 6.5×10^{19} molecules.

We have discussed at some length the form of crystals. One other property of crystals which distinguishes them from amorphous solids is that they always have a definite melting point, whereas amorphous solids soften over a range of temperature. This can easily be demonstrated by comparing ice and pitch — ice will always melt at $0\,°C$, but pitch softens and eventually becomes liquid over a range of tens of degrees. Another property that is important in distinguishing crystalline solids is that, when struck, they usually fracture along certain planes (called cleavage planes) which are parallel to the crystal faces. Thus mica, which has one very marked cleavage plane, breaks into thin sheets; rock salt, which has three cleavage planes at right angles, breaks into cubic or rectangular fragments. Amorphous solids, when broken, do not fracture along any particular plane but fracture with equal ease, or difficulty, in any direction.

3.10 Crystal growth

When crystals grow from a liquid, they form due to atoms or molecules attaching themselves in a regular pattern to small particles of solid. This initial solid form is called a *nucleus* and the first stage of formation of crystals, or *crystallization*, is called nucleation. This is followed by *growth*. Crystallization from the liquid can best be understood by considering it as a two-stage process of nucleation and growth.

3.11 Metals as crystalline materials

We have said in section 3.9 that, if it were possible to see the individual particles within a crystalline solid, we would expect to see ordered rows of atoms or molecules stretching in all directions. Such an arrangement is called a *space lattice*, and the nature of this pattern or space lattice determines most of the properties of the crystal and consequently most of the physical properties of the substance of which the crystal forms a part.

The use of X-rays to examine crystal structures has long been a technique favoured by chemists and physicists. X-rays are really radiation similar to light but with a wavelength of less than $\frac{1}{10\,000}$ that of visible light (see section 9). When they pass through crystals, they are diverted or *diffracted* to produce a series of spots, the pattern of which depends on the arrangement of the particles on the space lattice. This process of passing X-rays through a substance and examining the patterns produced is called *X-ray diffraction*.

When solid metals are examined by X-ray diffraction, they show regular patterns corresponding to certain crystal structures. A large number of common metals fall into one of three basic types of crystal structure and the properties of metals with similar crystal structures show considerable similarities. The three crystal structures concerned are called body-centred cubic, face-centred cubic, and close-packed hexagonal. These structures are shown in fig. A10.

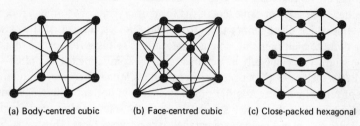

(a) Body-centred cubic   (b) Face-centred cubic   (c) Close-packed hexagonal

Fig. A10 The most common crystal structures of metals

Metals which have each of these crystal structures are shown in Table A4.

Body-centred cubic (b.c.c.)	Face-centred cubic (f.c.c.)	Close-packed hexagonal (c.p.h.)
Iron (below 910°C)	Aluminium	Titanium
Tungsten	Copper	Zinc
Chromium	Silver	Magnesium
Molybdenum	Iron (above 910 °C)	Cobalt
	Gold	
	Lead	

Table A4 Crystal structures of some common metals

It is interesting to note that metals with similar crystal structures tend to have similar properties with regard to their ability to be manipulated into shapes. The f.c.c. metals are all extremely malleable, even when cold, whereas the c.p.h. metals are not easily worked unless they are softened by heat.

When a molten metal is poured into a mould and is allowed to cool, it will start to solidify at the points where it is in contact with the mould, since the heat is extracted first at these positions. Groups of atoms arrange themselves in the crystal structure of the metal and grow as more atoms attach themselves. As the heat is conducted out of the metal in one direction, the growth of the solid material is usually in one direction. Solidification occurs at more than one point simultaneously and the areas of solid material which first appear grow in parallel, like columns. Because of this they are called *columnar grains* or columnar crystals. Eventually, when the heat flow is such that all the remaining

26

liquid metal is at the freezing temperature, it will also solidify, but without directional properties. If the metal is then taken from the mould, cut into sections, and polished, it would, after the distorted metal due to the cutting has been etched away with acids, show a structure similar to the one shown in fig. A11.

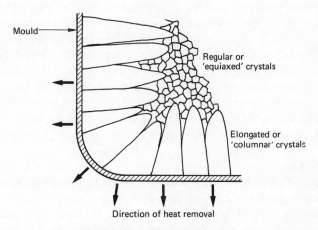

Fig. A11 Section of a metal which has solidified in a metal mould

If a metal has been worked by forging or rolling or a similar operation, the crystals, or 'grains' as the metallurgist usually calls them, are broken down within the metal but will reform or *recrystallize* on heating. Heavily distorted metal, e.g. aluminium that has been cold rolled, will look like fig. A12(a), but, if it is heated to 350 °C for some time, the grains will recrystallize and look like fig. A12(b). A material, such as a metal, that has many different crystals or grains in its structure is said to be *polycrystalline*. A great deal of the strength of metals is derived from this polycrystalline structure.

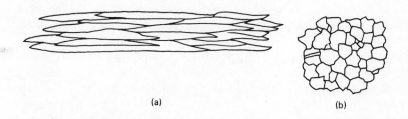

(a)

(b)

Fig. A12 (a) Heavily cold-worked aluminium, showing distorted grains
(b) Same aluminium as in (a) after heating

27

3.12 Alloys

If two or more metals are mixed in the molten state and are allowed to cool, they form what is known as an alloy. Brass is an alloy of copper and zinc, bronze is an alloy of copper and tin, and steel is an alloy mainly of iron, but with a little carbon and some or all of the following — manganese, chromium, nickel, sulphur, phosphorus, and traces of other elements. In many alloys, the atoms of the principal metal, e.g. copper in brass, may be replaced by atoms of one of the minor constituents, e.g. zinc, and under the microscope crystals similar to those of a pure metal but perhaps different in colour can be seen. This is because what is known as a *solid solution* has been formed. In a solid solution, some of the atoms of the solute replace atoms of the solvent (as in brass and bronze) or some of the atoms of the solute enter the spaces between the atoms of the solvent (as in carbon steels). The formation of solid solutions in alloys is one of the means whereby metallic mixtures may have their properties altered, and the study of this forms an important branch of metallurgy.

Exercise A4

1. If each of the following substances was added to water, state whether you would expect it to form a solution, a suspension, or neither: salt, pepper, oil, vinegar, alcohol, sawdust, lime, soap powder, sand, sugar, soot.
2. What do you understand by the term 'saturated solution'?
   How would you prepare a saturated solution of copper sulphate at room temperature? How would you prove that it was saturated?
3. Describe the process of crystallization from a solution, using sketches as appropriate.
4. What are the three most common crystal structures of metals? Illustrate your answer with sketches, and give three examples of each type.
5. What do you understand by the term 'polycrystalline material'? Sketch the structure of (a) a metal that has solidified in a mould, (b) a heavily worked metal, (c) a 'recrystallized' metal.

B   Energy

4 Energy, work, and power

For most people the terms 'energy' and 'work' have a meaning which is in no way scientific. However, both terms do have a precise scientific meaning and in this section we shall examine these terms and the relationship between the concepts they denote.

4.1 Fuels as a source of energy

When a fuel such as oil, coal, or gas is burnt, it produces large amounts of heat. This heat can be used to boil water and raise steam, and the steam may be used to drive turbines. We shall see in later sections that heat is a form of energy — the usefulness of a fuel is that it is a convenient way to store this energy, which can be utilized when required by simply burning the fuel.

4.2 Energy and work

To most people, work involves achieving some end, and in each of the following cases something is achieved as work is carried out. If a body is lifted vertically, work is done. If a spring is stretched or a piece of metal is bent, work is done. If a load is moved horizontally from rest, for example when a train starts to move, work is done. If we examine all these examples carefully it can be seen that they all have something in common — a force is required. In the first case the force is required to overcome gravity, in the second and third to overcome the resistance of the metal to a change in shape, and in the final example to overcome friction and to increase the speed of the train from a standing start. One other factor that all these examples have in common is motion. In each case the result of the force is movement of some kind.

In moving a force, a certain amount of work is carried out. In order to assess how much work a body is capable of, we need to define a new term, the *energy* of a body. When in everyday usage we describe someone as energetic or possessing energy, what we mean is that they are capable of carrying out more work than someone who is less energetic. The scientific definition is very similar:

> *energy is the ability to carry out work.*

4.3 Work done in relation to force

We have seen that in order to carry out work a force is needed and that there is some movement as a result of this force. The amount of work that is done is related to the magnitude of the force applied and the distance that is moved. This gives us a definition of the work done, which is as follows:

> *the work done by a force acting on a body is equal to the force applied multiplied by the distance through which the body moves in the direction of the force.*

4.4 The joule

The SI unit of work is named after J. P. Joule (1818–89), who studied the relationship between work and various types of energy. The *joule* (abbreviation J) is defined as *the work done when a force of 1 newton acts through a distance of 1 metre in the direction of the force:*

$$1 \text{ joule} = 1 \text{ newton} \times 1 \text{ metre}$$

This can be more easily understood if some examples are considered.

Example 1   Calculate the work done if a mass of 10 kg is lifted vertically from the ground to a height 2 m above the ground.

$$\text{Weight} = \text{mass} \times \text{acceleration due to gravity}$$

$$= 10 \text{ kg} \times 9.81 \text{ m/s}^2$$

$$= 98.1 \text{ N}$$

$\therefore$ Force to overcome gravity $= 98.1$ N

$$\text{Work done} = \text{force} \times \text{distance moved}$$

$$= 98.1 \text{ N} \times 2 \text{ m} = 196.2 \text{ J}$$

i.e. the work done in lifting the mass is 196.2 J.

Example 2   A mass of 6250 kg causes a steel cable to extend by 10 mm when suspended from its end. Calculate the work done in this extension.

$$\text{Weight} = \text{mass} \times \text{acceleration due to gravity}$$

$$= 6250 \text{ kg} \times 9.81 \text{ m/s}^2$$

$$= 61\,875 \text{ N}$$

$\therefore$ Force producing extension $= 61\,875$ N

$$\text{Extension} = 10 \text{ mm} = 10^{-2} \text{ m}$$

$$\text{Work done} = \text{force} \times \text{distance moved}$$

$$= 61\,875 \text{ N} \times 10^{-2} \text{ m} = 619 \text{ J}$$

i.e. the work done in producing the extension is 619 J.

4.5 Graphical representation of work done

When work is carried out by a force which moves through a given distance in the direction in which it is being applied, the amount of work may be represented on a graph by a work diagram, one side of which represents the distance moved, drawn to scale, and the other the force drawn to scale. Figure B1 shows

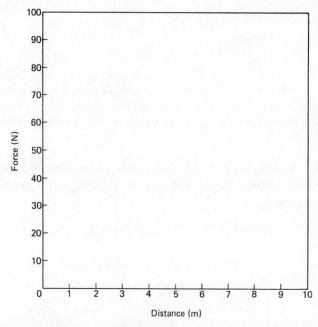

Fig. B1 Work represented by an area

how work can be represented on a graph. In this case a force of 100 N is represented by a scale on which 1 cm = 10 N. The force moves through 10 m, which is represented on a scale where 1 cm = 1 m. On this diagram, then, 1 cm^2 of area represents

$$10 \, N \times 1 \, m = 10 \, J$$

The sides of this diagram are each 10 cm, so the total area is

$$10 \times 10 = 100 \, cm^2$$

So the work done is represented by an area of 100 cm^2 on a scale of

$$1 \, cm^2 = 10 \, J$$

Therefore in this case the work done is given by

$$work \; done = 10 \, J/cm^2 \times 100 \, cm^2$$

31

$$= 1000 \text{ J}$$

$$= 1 \text{ kJ}$$

In this case the calculation of work done is very simple and the diagram provides no real advantage. It would have been just as easy to have multiplied the force by the distance moved:

$$\text{work done} = 100 \text{ N} \times 10 \text{ m}$$

$$= 1000 \text{ J}$$

$$= 1 \text{ kJ}$$

However, the principle that the area of the work diagram is equivalent to the work done is an important one and, when the force varies over the distance moved, the work diagram may be a much more convenient way of determining the work done.

Example 1 A coil spring in the relaxed condition is extended by 10 cm. Use a work diagram to calculate the work done if the spring requires a force of 5 N to extend it by 1 cm.

$$\text{Force to extend spring 10 cm} = 10 \text{ cm} \times 5 \text{ N/cm}$$

$$= 50 \text{ N}$$

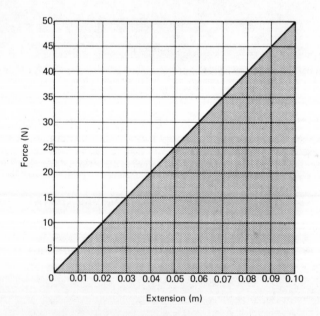

Fig. B2 Force—extension diagram for a coil spring

32

If we use the work diagram, fig. B2, the work done is given by the shaded area below the line. Each square on the diagram is equivalent to an amount of work which can be calculated as in fig. B1, that is by multiplying the vertical by the horizontal:

$$\text{work done represented by each square} = 5 \text{ N} \times 0.01 \text{ m}$$
$$= 0.05 \text{ J}$$
$$\text{total work done} = 45 \text{ whole squares} + 10 \text{ half squares}$$
$$= 50 \text{ whole squares}$$
$$= 50 \times 0.05 \text{ J}$$
$$= 2.5 \text{ J}$$

i.e. the work done in extending the spring is 2.5 J.

In example 1 the extension varied regularly with the force, but this is not always the case. If we consider a more complicated example, the value of work diagrams can be appreciated.

Example 2   A steel rod of length 50 mm is extended by applying an increasing load to it. The length of the rod measured as the load was increased is given in the following table of results:

Load (kN)	0	10	20	30	35	38	40
Length of rod (mm)	50	50.075	50.15	50.23	50.30	50.38	50.6

Calculate the work done in extending the rod by (a) 0.6 mm, (b) 0.2 mm.

In order to calculate the work done, we must first plot a graph of load against extension — fig. B3.

Each of the squares on this diagram represents work done as follows:

$$\text{work done} = \text{force (i.e. load)} \times \text{distance moved (i.e. extension)}$$
$$= 10 \text{ kN} \times 0.1 \text{ mm}$$
$$= 1 \text{ J}$$

So for the 12 whole squares below the line up to an extension of 0.6 mm, 12 J of work have been carried out. By counting the smaller divisions, the other incomplete squares will be found to add up to 5 whole ones, so that the total amount of work done in extending the rod by 0.6 mm is 12 + 5 = 17 J.

To calculate the work done in extending the rod by 0.2 mm we need to know the area below the line up to 0.2 mm on the horizontal scale. By counting squares, this can be found to be 2.5 J.

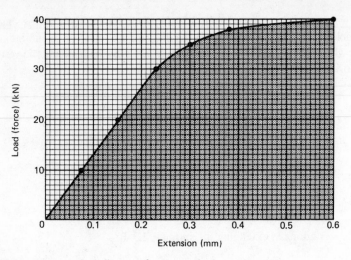

Fig. B3 Load–extension diagram for example 2, section 4.5

Exercise B1
1. Calculate the work done in lifting a mass of 350 kg to a height of 10 m.
2. A piece of metal suspended on a wire extends it by 3 mm. The work done in this extension is 88.3 J. What is the mass of the metal?
3. A helical spring is extended by a force which increases uniformly from zero to 1 kN. The spring extends by 250 mm. Draw a work diagram and determine the total work done.
4. A steel cable 100 m in length is suspended vertically from a drum. It has a mass of 2 kg per metre. Draw a work diagram to calculate the work done when the cable is wound on to the drum.
5. A vehicle starting from rest has the following forces in kilonewtons exerted on it at the distances shown from its initial position:

Distance from initial position (m)	0	5	10	15	20	25	30
Force (kN)	6.5	6.5	5.5	5.0	4.0	3.5	3.0

Draw a work diagram and determine the work done when the vehicle has moved (a) 30 m, (b) 20 m.

4.6 Forms of energy
There are several forms of energy. If a piece of metal is bent backwards and forwards, *mechanical energy* is used up in doing work and the metal will heat up. Similarly, if two pieces of metal are forced over each other, work is done in overcoming friction and there will be a rise in temperature. These are examples of *mechanical energy* being converted to *thermal energy* or heat energy. Other

34

forms of energy are *electrical energy, chemical energy, nuclear energy*, and *light energy*. Electrical energy is produced in a generator, such as a dynamo or alternator, when mechanical energy is used to move a magnetic field. Chemical energy is the energy that is liberated by a chemical reaction. Nuclear energy is the energy that is liberated when the structure of atoms changes.

The branch of science which deals with energy (in particular heat energy) is known as *thermodynamics*. A very important principle on which this science is based was first expressed by Joule and is sometimes called the *principle of conservation of energy* or the first law of thermodynamics. This states that *energy can be neither created nor destroyed*. This is a particularly important concept, because it enables the total amount of energy in a particular system to be accounted for accurately.

4.7 Conversion of energy

Although energy can be neither created nor destroyed, one form can be converted into another. For example, we have seen that mechanical energy can be converted into electrical energy by a generator. The reverse conversion is possible, as an electric motor converts electrical energy into mechanical energy. If a battery is charged with electricity (see section 24.1), chemical reactions occur on the plates and electrical energy is converted to chemical energy. When a battery discharges, as current is drawn off, the reverse occurs.

Heat energy is converted into mechanical energy in the steam engine and the internal-combustion engine, where the expansion of gases and vapours under the influence of heat causes a piston to move and produce mechanical energy. Heat energy can be produced by nuclear energy – heat is given off when the structure of atomic nuclei change. Nuclear reactors and nuclear weapons depend on this change. Heat energy is directly converted to electrical energy in a device known as a thermocouple – if two lengths of different metals are connected at one end and heated at this connection while the other ends are kept cold, an electric current is generated. The reverse of this effect, when electrical energy is converted to heat, is the principle on which the electric fire is based.

The conversion of one form of energy to another can be direct or through different stages. For example, fuels such as gas, oil, or coal contain a source of chemical energy. To convert this to electrical energy involves several stages and these can be more clearly understood by looking at fig. B4. In this diagram we can see how the chemical energy is converted to thermal energy by combustion of the fuel; this thermal energy in turn is used to produce mechanical energy which, through a turbine, can drive a dynamo and produce electrical energy. This electrical energy can then be converted into other forms of energy.

Despite all the changes in the type of energy, the total energy of the system can be accounted for – no energy is lost or created. If the total amount of energy leaving the system at the end is less than that produced by the original

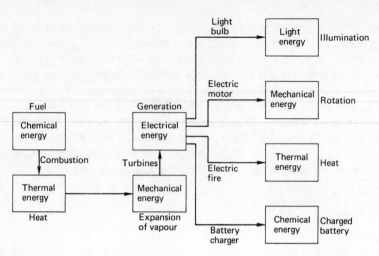

Fig. B4 Conversion of energy

combustion of the fuel, this is because some of the energy has been used to overcome friction, which will generate heat.

4.8 Efficiency

The term 'efficiency' has a meaning which, in the non-scientific sense, most people would understand. We say that a person or a process is more efficient than another if it produces more for a given amount of effort. The efficiency of a machine has a very similar meaning. If we define a *machine* as *a mechanical device for carrying out work by transmitting motion, force, and energy*, we can then arrive at a definition for efficiency.

Efficiency may be defined as *the ratio of the useful energy output to the energy input of a machine:*

$$\text{efficiency} = \frac{\text{useful output energy}}{\text{input energy}}$$

This ratio has no units and may be expressed either as a number or as a percentage (by multiplying by 100).

A perfect machine will have an efficiency of 1.0 or 100%, but most practical machines will have an efficiency considerably lower than this, as friction converts some of the mechanical-energy input to heat which is lost and will not do useful work or appear as useful output energy.

We shall look at some examples to make this idea clearer.

Example 1   A machine lifts a mass of 10 kg vertically through a height of 2 m when 0.39 kJ of energy are supplied to it. What is the efficiency of this machine?

36

Force to overcome gravity = mass x acceleration due to gravity

$$= 10 \text{ kg} \times 9.81 \text{ m/s}^2 = 98.1 \text{ N}$$

Work done in lifting mass = force x distance moved

$$= 98.1 \text{ N} \times 2 \text{ m}$$

$$= 196.2 \text{ J}$$

Energy input = 390 J

$$\text{Efficiency} = \frac{\text{useful output energy}}{\text{input energy}}$$

$$= \frac{196.2 \text{ J}}{390 \text{ J}} = 0.5$$

i.e. the efficiency of the machine is 0.5, or 50%.

Example 2   A machine for lifting a mass of 100 kg has 2 kJ of energy supplied to it. It has an efficiency of 60%. To what height will it lift this mass?

$$\text{Efficiency} = \frac{\text{useful output energy}}{\text{input energy}}$$

$$0.6 = \frac{\text{useful output energy}}{2000 \text{ J}}$$

Useful output energy = 0.6 x 2000 J

$$= 1200 \text{ J}$$

Work done = force x distance moved

$$1200 \text{ J} = (100 \times 9.81) \text{ N} \times \text{height}$$

$$\text{Height} = \frac{1200 \text{ J}}{100 \times 9.81 \text{ N}}$$

$$= \frac{1200 \text{ J}}{981 \text{ N}}$$

$$= 1.22 \text{ m}$$

i.e. the mass will be lifted 1.22 m.

4.9 Power

Power may be defined as *the rate of carrying out work* or *the rate of converting energy from one form into another* and can be considered as a measure of the work done per second. The SI unit of power is named after James Watt (1736–1819), a Scottish engineer. One *watt* (abbreviation W) is equal to *an energy conversion rate of 1 joule per second.*

For most engineering applications the watt is too small a unit so the kilowatt is commonly used as the unit of power.

Example 1   Calculate the power required to lift a mass of 500 kg through a height of 20 m in 30 seconds.

$$\text{Force required to lift mass} = 500 \text{ kg} \times 9.81 \text{ m/s}^2$$

$$= 4905 \text{ N}$$

$$\text{Work done} = \text{force} \times \text{distance moved}$$

$$= 4905 \text{ N} \times 20 \text{ m}$$

$$= 98\,100 \text{ J}$$

$$\text{Power} = \text{work done per second}$$

$$= \frac{98\,100 \text{ J}}{30 \text{ s}}$$

$$= 3270 \text{ W} = 3.27 \text{ kW}$$

i.e. the power required to lift the mass is 3.27 kW.

Example 2   To what height will a mass of 200 kg be lifted in 1 minute by a process that uses 1.5 kW?

$$\text{Force required to lift mass} = 200 \text{ kg} \times 9.81 \text{ m/s}^2$$

$$= 1962 \text{ N}$$

$$\text{Work done} = \text{force} \times \text{distance moved}$$

$$= 1962 \text{ N} \times h\text{m} = 1962 \, h \text{ J}$$

$$\text{Power} = \text{work done per second}$$

$$1500 \text{ W} = \frac{1962h \text{ J}}{60 \text{ s}}$$

$$h = \frac{1500 \times 60}{1962} = 45.9$$

i.e. the height lifted is 45.9 m.

The idea of power is also met in the study of electricity, and many electrical devices are given ratings in watts to indicate how rapidly they convert electrical energy into other forms of energy; for example, a 1 kilowatt electric fire will convert 1000 joules of electrical energy into heat energy and light energy every hour it is in use. A 40 watt light bulb will convert 40 joules of electrical energy into light energy and heat energy every hour, but a 40 watt fluorescent tube operates on a different principle which converts a smaller amount of the total electrical energy into heat and produces much more light energy. A 500 watt electrical motor will convert 500 joules of electrical energy into mechanical energy, heat energy (it gets hot) and sound energy (you can hear it running) every hour.

The power of electrical devices will be discussed further in section 12.

Exercise B2

1. List three different forms of energy and state how each of these forms of energy may be converted into the other two.
2. Figure B5 shows the layout of part of a motor vehicle. For each of the seven numbered stages shown, state what types of energy are involved and what they are being converted to (e.g. stage 2 – mechanical into electrical).

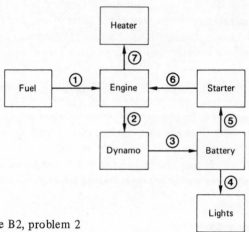

Fig. B5 Exercise B2, problem 2

3. The work done by a force which moves a body uniformly through 200 m in the direction of the force is 8 kJ. This work is carried out in 20 seconds. Calculate (a) the force, (b) the power.
4. A hoist, which is 30% efficient, uses 15 kW of power in 10 minutes uniform work. To what height will it raise a 10 tonne load in this time?
5. The power required to lift a load through 20 m in 10 seconds is 500 W. Calculate (a) the mass of the load, (b) the work done in lifting.
6. If 90 kJ of work are done in lifting 1 tonne of bricks in 3 minutes, (a) to what height are they lifted? (b) what power is used? Assume 100% efficiency.
7. A crane has an energy input of 20 kJ. To what height will it lift a 200 kg mass if it is 30% efficient?
8. A machine lifts a mass of 800 kg through a vertical height of 20 m. If 1236 kJ of energy are supplied to the machine to carry out this work, what is the

efficiency of the machine? If the work is carried out in 5 minutes, what power is used?

9. A locomotive hauls a train at 80 km/h and exerts a pull of 30 kN. Calculate (a) the work done in 10 minutes, (b) the power developed by the locomotive in this time.

5 Temperature measurement

'Temperature' and 'heat' are both terms in common use, but there is frequently confusion between their meanings.

In order to examine what is meant by these terms, let us first consider some examples. If two identical pans, one containing about twice as much water as the other, are placed on identical hot-plates, we would expect the pan with the least water to come to the boil first. Why?

If a block of metal at red heat is dropped into a litre of iced water, what happens to the metal? And to the water? If a piece of metal at the same temperature but half the size of the first is used, what differences will there be? If these experiments are repeated with twice as much water, what will be the effect?

Most people would be able to answer these questions and explain their answers by common sense, but in order to give a scientific explanation to these examples it is essential to be able to distinguish between two terms that are frequently wrongly used. If we say that one body has more heat in it than another, this is frequently taken to mean that it is hotter, but we will see that it can in fact be colder. If we say that one body has a higher temperature than another, does it necessarily mean that it has more heat in it?

5.1 Temperature and heat

If we go back to our first example — the two pans of water — the one with the least in it will boil first and, if both pans are removed from the heat source at the same time while they are boiling, the one with the least water in it will cool first. This means that it takes less heat from the hot-plate to boil it and consequently, when it is removed, less heat needs to be given off to the surroundings to allow it to cool. This indicates that heat depends on the mass of the substance involved and not solely on its temperature.

The temperature of the substance tells us how hot is is, not how much heat it contains.

One further point is illustrated by the pans of water. If they are left on the heat when they are at boiling point, the temperature of the water remains the same, but heat is still being supplied. This is an example of one of the conditions under which heat may be supplied to a body without raising its temperature. A similar phenomenon occurs when hot metal is put into iced water — no increase in temperature will occur in the water until all the ice has melted, so again heat is being supplied with no rise in temperature.

Temperature therefore is related to heat content but is not solely dependent on it. *Temperature may be defined as the degree of hotness or coldness of a substance.*

It will be observed from the experiments with the water and the hot metal that the temperature of the water rises and that of the metal falls until they become equal. They then remain the same and fall slowly as heat is given to the surroundings. This is shown in fig. B6. This gives us another view of temperature: it can be defined as *the property which decides whether heat flows into or out of a body.* If no heat flows between two substances when they are in contact with each other, they are said to be at the same temperature.

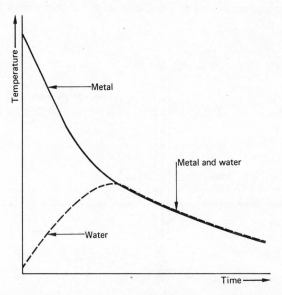

Fig. B6 The changes in temperature of a metal block and iced water

Heat is transmitted from the metal to the water and then eventually to the surrounding air. We have already seen that *heat is a form of energy* and a simple idea of its nature can be obtained by using a simplified view of the structure of matter. All matter consists of atoms or molecules arranged in a pattern in a solid or in a random distribution in a liquid or gas. These particles are not, however, completely stationary but tend to be in constant motion, about a fixed point in the case of a solid. As heat is supplied to the substance its effect is to increase the magnitude of this movement and the thermal energy is stored in the substance by this motion. As heat is removed, the vibration or motion is reduced.

41

5.2 Temperature scales

A very simple guide to the temperature of a substance is touch — we can normally feel which is the hotter of two substances. This is a very restricted means of temperature measurement, being confined to temperatures well below that of boiling water. It is also unreliable because the surfaces of difference substances feel different at the same temperature. This can be demonstrated by touching articles made from different materials (for example, wood, metal, or plastics) in the same room. The most common way of measuring temperature is to use an instrument known as a thermometer.

Ordinary thermometers rely on the fact that liquids expand when they are heated and contract when they are cooled and that this expansion and contraction is reproducible, so that a particular rise in temperature always produces exactly the same expansion in a given liquid. The two most common liquids used in thermometers are mercury and alcohol. A mercury thermometer is shown in fig. B7.

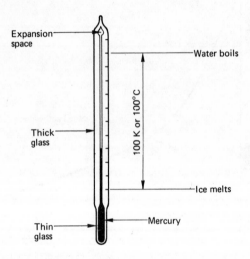

Fig. B7 Mercury thermometer

In order to decide which of two liquids is at the higher temperature, it is necessary only to immerse the bulb of the thermometer in each in turn and note how much the mercury expands. To make an assessment of temperature, the thermometer needs to be graduated in degrees. Several different temperature scales exist. The two most commonly used are the Celsius (formerly centigrade) and the Kelvin, or thermodynamic, scales. Other scales, which are becoming obsolete, are the Fahrenheit and Réamur scales.

The Celsius scale of temperature was devised by Anders Celsius in 1742. He used the melting temperature of ice and the boiling temperature of water as the basis for his scale, marking the position of the liquid in his thermometer as zero for freezing point and 100 degrees (100 °C) for boiling point. He then divided the space between these two points into 100 subdivisions (or centigrades), so that any temperature could be measured in terms of this system. On the Celsius scale, water boils at 100 °C, ice melts at 0 °C, iron melts at 1535 °C, copper melts at 1083 °C, platinum melts at 1774 °C, lead at 327 °C, and aluminium at 657 °C. On this scale mercury freezes below 0 °C, so minus temperatures are necessary to measure phenomena such as this. On the Celsius scale the freezing point of mercury is −39 °C.

The SI unit of temperature is not the degree Celsius but the kelvin (abbreviation K) named after the famous British scientist, Lord Kelvin (1824−1907). The unit is based on a scale on which no negative values are theoretically possible. This is known as the thermodynamic temperature scale or absolute scale. The zero value on this scale is the temperature at which a body would possess no thermal energy, which means that all its molecules or atoms would be stationary. It is also the temperature at which, in theory, the volume of an ideal gas, which would contract as it cooled, is zero. In practice this temperature is not attainable and, even if it were, it would not be possible to measure it. The divisions on this scale are the same size as degrees on the Celsius scale, so 1 °C (meaning one division on the Celsius scale) is equal to 1 K. The zero on the Kelvin scale corresponds to −273 °C, so the temperature at which ice melts, which is 0 °C, will equal 273 K and the boiling point of water, 100 °C, will be 373 K. To convert any temperature on the Celsius scale to kelvin all we have to do is to add 273. Consequently, the melting point of iron becomes 1808 K, of copper 1356 K, of platinum 2047 K, of lead 600 K, of aluminium 930 K, and of mercury 234 K.

5.3 Thermometers

We have already seen that one of the most convenient means of measuring temperature is to use the expansion of liquid in an enclosed container. The reason for enclosing the top of the thermometer is to prevent excessive evaporation. The earliest thermometers used the expansion of water, but this has several disadvantages, the chief of which are the restricted temperature range between the freezing and boiling points of water and also the fact that on heating from 0 °C water initially contracts before it expands. For an ideal thermometer liquid, the expansion with temperature should be as near linear as possible; that is, a one degree rise in temperature between, say, 15 °C and 16 °C should produce exactly the same expansion as a temperature rise between 85 °C and 86 °C.

Ethyl alcohol, which freezes at −112 °C, was then used as a thermometer liquid. This was popular due to its large expansion for a given temperature rise, but it has a marked disadvantage in that it boils at only 78 °C. To overcome this disadvantage, Fahrenheit (1686–1736), a German physicist, introduced mercury as a thermometric liquid. Mercury has a number of advantages over alcohol: it does not boil until a temperature of 357 °C is reached, although its freezing point (−39 °C) is not so low as that of alcohol; it very rapidly reaches the temperature it is required to measure, due to its high thermal conductivity; and it is opaque, so it can easily be seen. Also, mercury does not wet the sides of the tube. This is important because alcohol does wet the sides of the tube – this causes some to be left behind when measuring rapidly falling temperatures and this can cause low readings to be obtained.

The sensitivity of a thermometer depends on the bore of the capillary tube up which the liquid rises. A given temperature rise causes a certain increase in volume in the liquid. Consequently, the smaller the diameter of the capillary, the greater the distance along the tube the liquid moves for a given temperature increase.

When using a thermometer to measure the temperature of a liquid, it is important that the bulb is fully immersed in the liquid and that the liquid has been stirred to avoid differences in temperature throughout its bulk. On immersion, there will be a slight fall in the level of the mercury in a sensitive thermometer. This is due to the initial expansion of the glass. In order to obtain the most rapid response to changes in temperature, the glass of the bulb of the thermometer should be as thin as possible.

With age, the glass in a thermometer can change in shape and, as a result, a thermometer that was accurate when new can become less accurate as it ages. In order to be sure that accurate measurements of temperature are being made, it is advisable periodically to check the upper and lower fixed points on a mercury thermometer.

The lower fixed point is checked by placing the bulb of the thermometer in water containing pure melting ice. The upper fixed point is determined by placing the bulb of the thermometer in the steam from boiling water. As the temperature at which water boils depends on the atmospheric pressure, the upper fixed point should be measured at standard atmospheric pressure (see section 17).

Exercise B3

1. Distinguish between temperature and heat.

   A piece of iron of mass 500 g at a temperature of 300 °C was put into 5 litres of water at 70 °C. Sketch a graph showing the change in temperature of the iron and the water over a prolonged time and explain the shape of this graph.

2. On the same graph as in question 1, draw another curve for a piece of iron of 1 kg mass at 300 °C being immersed in 5 litres of water at 70 °C. Explain the differences in the shape of these curves.

3. The scale on a mercury thermometer has accidentally been obliterated. Explain how you would go about measuring the boiling point of an unknown liquid, using this thermometer.

4. An ungraduated thermometer shows a mercury height of 73 mm in melting ice, and 268 mm in steam above boiling water. When immersed in a mixture of salt and ice it shows a height of 40 mm, and in molten solder 473 mm. In the air it reads 95 mm.

What is the temperature of (a) the salt and ice mixture? (b) the solder? (c) the air?

6 Specific heat capacity and latent heat

In this section we shall see that the effect of heat on different substances is not the same. A given amount of heat will have a different effect on the temperature of different substances, and in some cases it is possible to supply heat to a substance without raising its temperature.

6.1 Specific heat capacity

We have already said that heat is a form of energy (section 4.6), sometimes called thermal energy. The units that are to be used to measure quantities of heat must be energy units, and the SI energy unit is the joule.

The effect of a given amount of heat on the temperature of a particular substance in a particular state (i.e. solid, liquid, or gas) is expressed as the specific heat capacity of that substance.

In general, *the specific heat capacity of a substance is the quantity of heat or thermal energy required to raise the temperature of 1 kg of that substance by 1°C.*

For most applications it can be assumed that the heat necessary to raise the temperature of 1 kg of water by 1 °C is 4190 J or 4.19 kJ, so we can say that the specific heat capacity of water is 4.19 kilojoules per kilogram per degree Celsius (4.19 kJ/kg °C). Different substances have difference specific heat capacities and the value of the specific heat capacity for some common substances is given in Table B1.

6.2 Specific-heat problems

In solving problems involving thermal energy and specific heat capacity, we use the formula

$$Q = mct$$

where Q is the thermal energy in joules (or kilojoules),

m is the mass of substance in kilograms,

c is the specific heat capacity in joules (or kilojoules) per kilogram per °C,

t is the temperature change in °C.

Substance	Specific heat capacity (kJ/kg °C)
Aluminium	0.95
Brass	0.40
Iron	0.5
Copper	0.39
Ice	2.1
Lead	0.13
Paraffin	29.7
Water	4.19
Zinc	0.4

Table B1 Specific heat capacities of some common substances

We can use this formula to solve the majority of problems, provided that there is no change of state involved (e.g. solid to liquid or liquid to gas).

Example 1 Calculate the quantity of heat required to raise the temperature of 10 kg of water from 0 °C to 100 °C.

In this case m = 10 kg, c = 4.19 kJ/kg °C, t = 100–0 = 100 °C

$$Q = mct$$
$$= 10 \text{ kg} \times 4.19 \text{ kJ/kg} °C \times 100 °C$$
$$= 4.19 \times 10^3 \text{ kJ} = 4.19 \text{ MJ}$$

i.e. 4.19 MJ of heat are required.

Example 2 Calculate the quantity of heat required to raise the temperature of 2 kg of copper from 200 °C to 250 °C.

m = 2 kg, c = 390 J/kg °C, t = 250 – 200 = 50 °C

$$Q = mct$$
$$= 2 \text{ kg} \times 390 \text{ J/kg} °C \times 50 °C$$
$$= 39\,000 \text{ J} = 39 \text{ kJ}$$

i.e. 39 kJ of heat are required.

Example 3 What would be the final temperature if 50 kJ of heat were supplied to 2.29 kg of an oil at 5 °C, if the specific heat capacity of the oil is 2.18kJ/kg°C?

m = 2.29 kg, c = 2.18 kJ/kg °C, Q = 50 kJ

$$Q = mct$$

$$50 \text{ kJ} = 2.29 \text{ kg} \times 2.18 \text{ kJ/kg}\,^{\circ}\text{C} \times t$$

$$t = \frac{50 \text{ kJ}}{2.29 \text{ kg} \times 2.18 \text{ kJ/kg}\,^{\circ}\text{C}} = 10\,^{\circ}\text{C}$$

Rise in temperature $= 10\,^{\circ}\text{C}$

so final temperature will be $15\,^{\circ}\text{C}$.

Example 4 A piece of copper is raised in temperature from $10\,^{\circ}\text{C}$ to $60\,^{\circ}\text{C}$ by the addition of 195 kJ of heat energy. Calculate the mass of the copper if its specific heat capacity is 0.39 kJ/kg $^{\circ}$C.

$c = 0.39 \text{ kJ/kg}\,^{\circ}\text{C}, \ t = 50\,^{\circ}\text{C}, \ Q = 195 \text{ kJ}$

$$Q = mct$$

$$195 \text{ kJ} = m \times 0.39 \text{ kJ/kg}\,^{\circ}\text{C} \times 50\,^{\circ}\text{C}$$

$$m = \frac{195 \text{ kJ}}{0.39 \text{ kJ/kg}\,^{\circ}\text{C} \times 50\,^{\circ}\text{C}} = 10 \text{ kg}$$

i.e. the mass of the copper is 10 kg.

The above are quite simple straightforward examples using the formula $Q = mct$. More complicated problems may be solved if the calculation is broken down into simple steps.

Example 5 When 1 cubic metre of gas is burnt, it gives off 16 MJ of heat energy. If a heat-treatment furnace uses 55% of this heat energy to heat aluminium billets, calculate the mass of aluminium that can be heated from $12\,^{\circ}\text{C}$ to $162\,^{\circ}\text{C}$ when 10 m^3 of gas are burnt.

The specific heat capacity of aluminium is 950 J/kg $^{\circ}$C.

The heat energy produced by burning 10 m^3 of gas $= 16 \times 10$ MJ

If 55% of this heat is used in heating the aluminium,

$Q = 16 \times 10 \times 0.55 \times 10^3 \text{ kJ}$

$c = 0.95 \text{ kJ/kg}\,^{\circ}\text{C} \qquad t = 150\,^{\circ}\text{C}$

$$Q = mct$$

$$16 \times 10 \times 0.55 \times 10^3 \text{ kJ} = m \times 0.95 \text{ kJ/kg}\,^{\circ}\text{C} \times 150\,^{\circ}\text{C}$$

$$m = \frac{16 \times 10 \times 0.55 \times 10^3 \text{ kJ}}{0.95 \text{ kJ/kg}\,^{\circ}\text{C} \times 150\,^{\circ}\text{C}} = 617.5 \text{ kg}$$

i.e. the mass of aluminium is 617.5 kg.

We have considered several examples in which the addition of heat has been shown to cause the temperature of liquids or solids to rise, and we have seen how temperature decides in which direction heat will flow. Later in this section we shall examine the methods by which heat is transferred, but for the present it is sufficient to know that, when a hot substance and a colder one come together, heat will pass from the hotter substance to the cooler one until the two substances are at the same temperature. This is true whether the substances are solid, liquid, or gaseous.

If we take an example, it will be easier to account for the changes in temperature that occur when hot and cold substances are mixed. Let us look first at what happens if a piece of copper of mass 1 kg at a temperature of 200 °C is put into 1 kg of water at 10 °C contained in an aluminium container of mass 300 g.

The temperature of the copper will fall to a temperature θ °C and that of the water and aluminium container will rise to θ °C. When the temperatures are equal, no heat can flow in either direction. If we examine each of the components in the system we can see that the copper has lost some heat, which will depend on its mass, its specific heat capacity, and the fall in temperature.

The fall in temperature of the copper, if it starts at a temperature of 200 °C and ends up at a temperature of θ °C, is $(200 - \theta)$ °C and the heat lost by it is

$$Q_c = m \times c \times t = 1 \times 0.39 \times (200 - \theta) \text{ kJ}$$

The water and its container will rise to a temperature of θ °C, which means that their temperature rise will be $(\theta - 10)$ °C.

If we call the heat gained by the water Q_w,

$$Q_w = m \times c \times t = 1 \times 4.19 \times (\theta - 10) \text{ kJ}$$

and the heat gained by the aluminium container (Q_a) will be given by

$$Q_a = m \times c \times t = 0.3 \times 0.95 \times (\theta - 10) \text{ kJ}$$

If we assume that no heat is lost to or picked up from the surroundings, the heat that is gained by the water and the container can come only from the copper. That is to say that the heat lost by the hotter object is equal to the heat gained by the cooler. This means that

$$Q_c = Q_w + Q_a$$

If we give the values to each of these terms that we have already worked out, we should be able to calculate the resultant temperature.

If $Q_c = Q_w + Q_a$,

$$1 \times 0.39 \times (200 - \theta) \text{ kJ} = 1 \times 4.19 \times (\theta - 10) \text{ kJ} + 0.3 \times 0.95 \times (\theta - 10) \text{ kJ}$$

$$(78 - 0.39\theta) = (4.19\theta - 41.9) + (0.285\theta - 2.85)$$

48

$$4.765\theta = 122.75$$

$$\theta = \frac{122.75}{4.765} = 25.8$$

i.e. the final temperature of the mixture will be 25.8 °C.

The calculation we have just carried out illustrates a very important principle — when a hot and a cold substance are brought together, the temperatures become the same and heat lost by the hotter substance is equal to that gained by the colder one. (It is assumed that no heat is lost or gained by the surroundings.)

We will work through one more example to illustrate this principle.

Example 6 A copper cylinder of mass 5 kg contains 10 kg of water at 70 °C. Calculate the amount of water at 5 °C that has to be added to the cylinder to reduce the temperature to 60 °C.

If the temperature of the cylinder and water are reduced to 60 °C, the heat lost by the water is Q_w = 10 kg x 4.19 kJ/kg °C x 10 °C and the heat lost by the cylinder is Q_c = 5 kg x 0.39 kJ/kg °C x 10 °C.

If we call the mass of the cold water M, then the heat gained by this cold water is

$$Q_{cw} = M \times 4.19 \text{ kJ/kg}°C \times 55°C$$

If heat gained = heat lost,

$$Q_{cw} = Q_w + Q_c$$

$$M \times 4.19 \text{ kJ/kg}°C \times 55°C = (10 \text{ kg} \times 4.19 \text{ kJ/kg}°C \times 10°C)$$

$$+ (5 \text{ kg} \times 0.39 \text{ kJ/kg}°C \times 10°C)$$

$$= 419 \text{ kJ} + 19.5 \text{ kJ}$$

$$= 438.5 \text{ kJ}$$

$$\therefore \quad M = \frac{438.5 \text{ kJ}}{4.19 \text{ kJ/kg}°C \times 55°C} = 1.81 \text{ kg}$$

So 1.81 kg of water at 5 °C will bring the temperature of the hot water and cylinder down to 60 °C.

Exercise B4
1. Calculate the amount of heat required to raise the temperature of 50 kg of water from 10 °C to 50 °C.
2. Calculate the amount of heat required to raise the temperature of 5 kg of copper from 150 °C to 250 °C.

3. What is the rise in temperature that would be produced if 150 kJ of heat were supplied to 4.58 kg of paraffin?

4. What is the mass of a piece of iron whose temperature increases from 0 °C to 500 °C by the addition of 195 MJ of thermal energy?

5. A fuel gas, when burnt, gives rise to 20 MJ of heat for every cubic metre of gas burnt. What temperature rise could be produced in 1 tonne of copper ingots if 15 m^3 of this gas are burnt in a furnace which transmits 60% of the available heat to the copper?

6. An iron bucket has a mass of 2.5 kg and contains 6.5 kg of water at 5 °C. To what temperature will the bucket and the water be raised if 1.5 kg of water at 95 °C are added to it?

7. An aluminium container holds 4.2 kg of water at 68 °C. A piece of iron of mass 6 kg at a temperature of 220 °C is put into the water, and the temperature of the water rises to 75 °C. What is the mass of the aluminium container?

8. A brass pan contains 22 kg of water at 15 °C. If the mass of the brass is 8 kg, calculate the quantity of water at 85 °C that has to be added to double the temperature of the pan and its contents.

9. An aluminium drum of mass 6.5 kg has an iron plug of mass 0.5 kg and contains 13.1 kg of water at 98 °C. How much water at 2 °C has to be added to reduce the temperature of the whole system to 75 °C?

10. A copper container of mass 0.5 kg contains 0.5 kg of water at 2 °C. To it is added 0.25 kg of water at 16 °C, 1 kg of copper at 100 °C, and 0.5 kg of iron at 210 °C. Calculate the final temperature.

6.3 Sensible heat and latent heat

If a pan of water is put on a hot-plate and heat is supplied by the hot-plate, the heat is taken up by the water and the temperature of the water will rise. We have already seen that the rise in temperature depends on the mass of the water, its specific heat capacity, and the amount of heat energy supplied. The heat that is being put into the water is having an easily detectable effect — it is causing a rise in temperature. Heat of this kind is known as *sensible heat*, because it can be detected by the sense of touch.

There is heat of a different kind, however. If the pan of water is left on the hot-plate, its temperature will keep on rising until, under normal conditions, it reaches 100 °C, when, despite the fact that heat is still being supplied to it, it will remain at the same temperature. It will start to boil, and its temperature will stay at 100 °C until all the water has changed to steam. This particular phenomenon was first investigated thoroughly by Joseph Black (1728–99), who attempted to discover what happened to this heat that did not cause a rise in temperature. Because it did not have the normal effect that heat has of increasing the temperature, it remained hidden and he called it *latent heat*.

A similar phenomenon could be investigated if we were to take a piece of ice out of a refrigerator at −30 °C and apply a source of heat to it. Its temperature would rise steadily until it reached the melting point of ice, 0 °C. The ice would then remain at the same temperature, even though heat was passing into it. When eventually all the ice had melted, the temperature of the water produced would rise steadily. Sensible heat is supplied to the ice, causing its temperature to rise, and latent heat is then used up not in producing a temperature rise but in causing a change in state from ice to water at the same temperature.

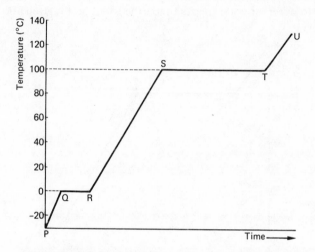

Fig. B8 Change in temperature of ice, water, and steam with time

These ideas are easier to understand if we study fig. B8, which shows how the temperature of a block of ice changes with time, due to the effect of heat being supplied to it at a constant rate. If the ice starts off at −30 °C, the point represented by P on the curve, it will rise in temperature to 0 °C along the line PQ. It will remain at 0 °C for the time represented by QR until it has all melted, so at point Q we have ice at 0 °C and at R water at 0 °C, and between Q and R a mixture of ice and water. As further heat is supplied, the water will rise in temperature to 100 °C, point R, where it will start to boil. Under normal conditions, the temperature will then remain constant again for the time represented by ST, until at T the water will all have been converted to steam. If heat is supplied to the steam it will rise in temperature along TU, giving *superheated steam.*

So, on the graph in fig. B8 we can see three examples of sensible heat (represented by PQ, RS, and TU) and two examples of latent heat (QR and ST).

This latent heat, which is a form of energy, is used up in rearranging the molecules to effect the changes in state.

Latent heat which is used in melting a substance (in this case ice) is called *latent heat of fusion* (from the Latin '*fusus*', meaning molten).

Latent heat which is used in vaporizing a substance is called *latent heat of vaporization.*

We have seen examples of how latent heat is absorbed by a substance when it changes its state from solid to liquid or from liquid to vapour. As heat is a form of energy and as energy can be neither created nor destroyed, it must be stored within a substance when that substance changes its state from solid to liquid or from liquid to gas. If the changes of state are reversed, that is if steam condenses to water, or water freezes to ice, the latent heat is given off.

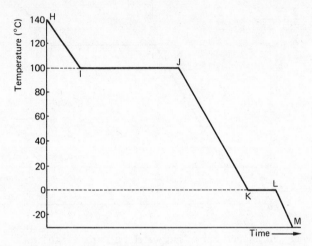

Fig. B9 Cooling of superheated steam

Figure B9 shows what happens when superheated steam is cooled to temperatures below the freezing point of water. If the temperature is measured at regular intervals and the results are plotted against time, the following points should be noted. Between H and I the steam cools regularly until it reaches the boiling point of water. It then remains at a constant temperature for a period of time represented by IJ, even though it is still giving off heat. When all the steam at 100 °C has changed to water at 100 °C, it starts to cool again uniformly until it reaches its freezing point, 0 °C, represented by K. From K to L its temperature remains constant until all the liquid is converted to ice, and it then cools along LM.

All substances that change in state from solid to liquid or from liquid to vapour will behave in the same way. If heat is supplied to iron, its temperature will rise until it reaches 1535 °C when it will remain constant until all the iron is liquid. Then the temperature will start to rise again. If molten aluminium is cooled from 700 °C its temperature will fall regularly to 660 °C, when it will remain constant until all the latent heat is given out, after which it will continue to fall.

52

6.4 Specific latent heat

The amount of heat needed to change a solid into a liquid at its melting point will depend on the amount of solid involved. A large block of ice will require more heat than a small one; similarly, a large volume of water will need more heat to boil it away than a smaller one — a proposition that can easily be checked by using two pans of water on a cooker, one full and one half full.

In order to carry out calculations on the amount of heat required for these changes of state, a fixed mass of liquid or solid must be considered. The standard mass of 1 kg is used and the *specific latent heat of fusion* can be defined as *the heat required to change 1 kg of the substance from the solid state to the liquid state at the same temperature.*

Similarly, the *specific latent heat of vaporization* of a substance can be defined as *the heat required to change 1 kg of the substance from the liquid to the vapour state at the same temperature.*

The specific latent heat of fusion of ice is 335 kJ/kg, that is when 1 kg of ice at 0 °C melts completely to water at 0 °C it absorbs 335 kJ of thermal energy.

The specific latent heat of vaporization of water is 2257 kJ/kg (2.257 MJ/kg), that is when 1 kg of water at 100 °C boils completely to steam at 100 °C it absorbs 2257 kJ of thermal energy.

The difference in these values is due to the fact that much more energy is necessary to convert water to steam than to convert ice to water, since when a vapour is produced it needs to do work against its surroundings to allow for the large expansion in volume. If we examine our graph of temperature against time for heat being supplied to ice and water at a constant rate (fig. B8), we can see that the difference in the heat supplied is shown by the different lengths of QR and ST.

6.5 Problems

In order to understand more fully the idea of latent heat we shall consider some examples.

Example 1   How much heat is needed completely to melt 6.5 kg of ice at 0 °C?

$$\text{Quantity of heat required} = \text{mass} \times \text{specific latent heat of fusion of ice}$$

$$= 6.5 \text{ kg} \times 335 \text{ kJ/kg}$$

$$= 2177.5 \text{ kJ}$$

i.e. to melt 6.5 kg of ice and convert it to water at 0 °C, 2177.5 kJ of heat are required.

Example 2   Calculate the heat necessary to convert 4 kg of ice with an initial temperature of −10 °C completely to water at 0 °C.

Heat necessary to raise temperature of ice from $-10\,°C$ to $0\,°C$

$$= \text{mass x specific heat capacity x temperature rise}$$

$$= 4\text{ kg} \times 2.1\text{ kJ/kg}\,°C \times 10\,°C$$

$$= 84\text{ kJ}$$

Heat necessary to melt 4 kg of ice at $0\,°C$

$$= \text{mass x specific latent heat of fusion}$$

$$= 4\text{ kg} \times 335\text{ kJ/kg}$$

$$= 1340\text{ kJ}$$

Total heat required $= 84\text{ kJ} + 1340\text{ kJ} = 1424\text{ kJ}$

i.e. to convert 4 kg of ice at $-10\,°C$ to water at $°C$, 1424 kJ of heat are required.

Example 3   A block of ice of mass 1 kg is at $-2\,°C$, and 425 kJ of thermal energy are supplied to it. Calculate the temperature of the resultant water.

The heat that is supplied to the ice will be used in three separate ways:

a) to raise the temperature of the ice to $0\,°C$,
b) to melt the ice,
c) to raise the temperature of the water produced by melting.

We can best solve the problem by considering each of these stages in turn.

a) Heat required to raise the temperature of the ice

$$= \text{mass x specific heat capacity x temperature rise}$$

$$= 1\text{ kg} \times 2.1\text{ kJ/kg}\,°C \times 2\,°C$$

$$= 4.2\text{ kJ}$$

b) Heat required to melt the ice

$$= \text{mass x specific latent heat of fusion}$$

$$= 1\text{ kg} \times 335\text{ kJ/kg}$$

$$= 335\text{ kJ}$$

c) Heat used in raising temperature of the water

$$= \text{mass x specific heat capacity x temperature}$$

If we call the final temperature $\theta\,°C$,

heat used $= 1\text{ kg} \times 4.19\text{ kJ/kg}\,°C \times \theta\,°C$

The ice had 425 kJ of heat supplied to it. In raising the temperature to $0\,^\circ\mathrm{C}$ and in melting the ice, 339.2 kJ have been used. This leaves

$$425 - 339.2 = 85.8 \text{ kJ left to raise the temperature of the water}$$

so the heat used in raising the water temperature is

$$85.8\,\text{kJ} = 1\,\text{kg} \times 4.19\,\text{kJ/kg}\,^\circ\mathrm{C} \times \theta\,^\circ\mathrm{C}$$

so $\qquad \theta = \dfrac{85.8}{4.19} = 20.5$

i.e. the final temperature of the water will be $20.5\,^\circ\mathrm{C}$.

From the above examples we can see that, in attempting to solve problems of this type, it is important to break down the problem into individual stages and to calculate the relationships between heat, specific heat capacity, specific latent heat, mass, and temperature for each individual stage. This will result in an equation from which the required quantity, whether it be temperature, mass, or amount of heat, can be obtained.

The same techniques are applied to more complicated problems, which may require more stages. The following examples are used to illustrate these principles.

Example 4 A block of ice of mass 5 kg at $-10\,^\circ\mathrm{C}$ is put into 10 kg of water at $80\,^\circ\mathrm{C}$ in a copper container which has a mass of 1 kg. Calculate the final temperature of the water when all the ice has melted.

Call the final temperature $\theta\,^\circ\mathrm{C}$.

Heat gained by the ice

$$= \text{heat gained in rising from } -10\,^\circ\mathrm{C} \text{ to } 0\,^\circ\mathrm{C}$$

$$+ \text{ latent heat of fusion}$$

$$+ \text{ heat gained in rising from } 0\,^\circ\mathrm{C} \text{ to } \theta\,^\circ\mathrm{C}$$

$$= \text{mass} \times \text{specific heat capacity of ice} \times \text{temperature rise}$$

$$+ \text{ mass} \times \text{specific latent heat of fusion}$$

$$+ \text{ mass} \times \text{specific heat capacity of water} \times \text{temperature rise}$$

$$= (5\,\text{kg} \times 2.1\,\text{kJ/kg}\,^\circ\mathrm{C} \times 10\,^\circ\mathrm{C}) + (5\,\text{kg} \times 335\,\text{kJ/kg})$$

$$+ (5\,\text{kg} \times 4.19\,\text{kJ/kg}\,^\circ\mathrm{C} \times \theta\,^\circ\mathrm{C})$$

Heat lost by the water and its container

$$= \text{heat lost by the water} + \text{heat lost by the copper}$$

$$= \text{mass} \times \text{specific heat capacity of water} \times \text{temperature fall}$$
$$+ \text{mass} \times \text{specific heat capacity of copper} \times \text{temperature fall}$$
$$= [10 \text{ kg} \times 4.19 \text{ kJ/kg}\,^\circ\text{C} \times (80 - \theta)\,^\circ\text{C}]$$
$$+ [1 \text{ kg} \times 0.39 \text{ kJ/kg}\,^\circ\text{C} \times (80 - \theta)\,^\circ\text{C}]$$

Heat gained by the ice = heat lost by the water and by the container

$$(5 \times 2.1 \times 10)\,\text{J} + (5 \times 335)\,\text{J} + (5 \times 4.19 \times \theta)\,\text{J}$$
$$= [10 \times 4.19 \times (80 - \theta)]\,\text{J} + [1 \times 0.39 \times (80 - \theta)]\,\text{J}$$
$$105 + 1675 + 20.95\theta = 3352 - 41.9\theta + 31.2 - 0.39\theta$$
$$63.24\theta = 1603.2$$
$$\theta = \frac{1603.2}{63.24} = 25.4$$

i.e. the final temperature is 25.4 $^\circ$C.

Example 5 An oil burner produces 900 MJ of heat per hour. Calculate the amount of water at 10 $^\circ$C that can be completely converted to steam at 100 $^\circ$C in two hours by this burner if 80% of the heat is transmitted to the water.

Let the mass of water that can be boiled $= m$ kg. If H is the amount of heat required to raise the temperature of the water from 10 $^\circ$C to 100 $^\circ$C,

H = mass of water $\times$ specific heat capacity $\times$ temperature rise

$= m$ kg $\times$ 4.19 kJ/kg $^\circ$C $\times$ 90 $^\circ$C

If L is the amount of heat required to convert m kg of water at 100 $^\circ$C to steam at 100 $^\circ$C,

L = mass of water $\times$ specific latent heat of vaporization

$= m$ kg $\times$ 2257 kJ/kg

Total heat required $= (H + L)$ kJ

In two hours the burner gives out heat to the water at 80% efficiency:

2h $\times$ 900 MJ/h $\times$ 0.80 = 720 MJ of heat

So in order to raise m kg of water from 10 $^\circ$C to 100 $^\circ$C and boil it completely, $(H + L)$ kJ is required and the heat supplied is 720 MJ or 720×10^3 kJ. So $(H + L)$ must equal 720×10^3 kJ.

$\therefore$ (m kg $\times$ 4.19 kJ/kg $^\circ$C $\times$ 90 $^\circ$C) + (m kg $\times$ 2257 kJ/kg) = 720×10^3 kJ

$$m = \frac{720 \times 10^3}{2634.1} = 273.34$$

i.e. in two hours the burner will completely convert to steam 273.34 kg of water at 10°C.

Exercise B5

1. Calculate the amount of heat required to raise the temperature of 10 kg of ice at −20°C and convert it completely to water at 15°C.
2. If 5 kg of ice at −5°C are put into 5 kg of water at 80°C, what will be the ultimate temperature of the mixture?
3. A copper cylinder of mass 1.5 kg contains 15 kg of water at 10°C. How much heat is required to convert half of this water to steam?
4. An aluminium cylinder of mass 2.25 kg contains 10 kg of water at 0°C on top of which is 1.25 kg of ice also at 0°C. How much hot water at 90°C must be added to the cylinder to bring it and its contents up to 10°C?
5. A brass cylinder of mass 250 g holds 500 g of water. They are at 10°C. What mass of iron at 700°C must be dropped into the cylinder to cause 20 g of the water to boil away?
6. A mixture of ice and water whose total mass is 10 kg is in a copper tank of mass 1.5 kg and has a piece of iron of mass 4 kg at a temperature of 600°C put into it. The water temperature rises to 15°C. What were the masses of ice and water respectively?
7. Steam at a temperature of 100°C is blown on to an iron plate of mass 500 g at a rate of 10 kg every 20 minutes. Assuming that 70% of the steam condenses on the plate, how long will it take for its temperature to rise from 10°C to 100°C?
8. An aluminium can of mass 750 g containing 1.5 kg of water and 200 g of ice is placed on a brass hot-plate at 400°C which is immediately turned off. If the mass of the hot-plate is 1200 g, what will be the resulting temperature of the can of water if 75% of its heat enters the water?

7 Heat transfer

In the preceding sections we have looked at various effects caused by bringing substances at different temperatures into contact with each other. We have seen that heat moves or is transferred from the hotter substance to the colder one. In this section we shall explain how heat is transferred from one part of a body to a different part. We shall see that there is more than one way in which heat moves. These ways can be better understood if we look at some examples.

7.1 Conduction, convection, and radiation

Conduction

If we put one end of a copper rod in a flame, after a very short time the end away from the flame will become warm and eventually unbearably hot, even though it started quite cold to the touch. Heat has been transferred from the hot flame along the rod from the hot end to the cold. If it were possible to examine the rod in sufficient detail to look at its actual atoms, we could explain this phenomenon.

At the end of the copper in the flame, the heat causes the copper atoms to vibrate as they take up thermal energy from the flame. These vibrating atoms in turn cause the atoms next to them to vibrate, and this increase in motion is passed rapidly along the rod, giving the sensation of heat moving along the rod. The speed at which heat is transferred and the distance that it can travel by this method depend on the amount of thermal energy that is supplied to the end of the rod and the arrangement of the atoms inside the rod. This is why different materials allow heat to pass along them at different rates and to different extents.

This method of heat transfer can also occur between two different bodies. This is what happens if an aluminium pan is placed on a steel hot-plate of a cooker — the thermal vibrations due to the heat in the steel are conducted to the aluminium and then to the contents of the pan.

The process of heat transfer that we have just described is known as *conduction*, and this is defined as *the transfer of heat from one part of a body to another, or from one body to another, by the transfer of heat energy within the atoms or molecules, with no detectable motion of the body.*

Convection

A completely different means of heat transfer can operate when liquids or gases are involved. If, just after it has been switched on, you put your hands on the outside of an electric kettle, which has the element in the bottom, you will find that the top becomes hotter much more rapidly than the bottom, and in fact the region under the element stays cool even when the top of the kettle is too hot to touch. Central-heating radiators always heat up at the top first, even though the hot water enters at the bottom. If a lighted cigarette is placed in an ashtray in the centre of a room where heating has just been turned on, the smoke can be seen to rise, spread along the ceiling, and then descend at the edges of the room. If you examine a glass beaker of water that has just been put on to a hot-plate, it is possible to see currents of moving water circulating.

The process of heat transference that is occurring in the above examples is. known as *convection*, which is the name given to *transfer of heat through a substance by the actual movement of the substance itself.*

What is in fact happening is that, as the water or air heats up, its density changes, it becomes lighter and rises, and colder material comes in to take its place. This explains why the water below the element in the kettle or at the bottom of the radiator, or the air nearest to the floor, is the last to heat up.

Radiation
There is a third means of heat transfer that is different from the other two methods in that the hot body and the colder one, or the hot part of a body and the colder part, do not come into contact. It is by this means that the heat of the sun can reach us on Earth across millions of kilometres of space which contain no solid to conduct the heat and no air or gas to allow convection. On a smaller scale this method of heat transfer can be illustrated if a piece of red-hot metal is suspended above a sheet of paper. The paper will blacken, smoulder, and could even catch fire, due to heat being transferred from the metal. This method of transfer can not be conduction, as the paper and the metal are not touching. It can not be convection, as the hot air heated by the metal will rise. In this case the method of heat transference is known as *radiation,* which is *the transfer of heat due to the motion of waves in the space between the hot and cold substances.* The motion of waves is discussed in section 9.

Heat radiation is similar in character to radio or television waves or light waves except that its frequency of vibration is different. Waves are given out or emitted by the hot body and are transmitted through space, whether this space contains air or not, and they are not detected until they fall on to another body.

7.2 Examples of heat transference
Conduction is used to transfer heat in a variety of systems. Domestic cooking utilizes the conduction of heat through metal saucepans or dishes from the heat source to the contents. Central heating requires the metal of the radiator to conduct heat from the hot water inside the system to the air of the room to be heated.

An experiment that can be carried out in the laboratory is illustrated in fig. B10. In this experiment, rods of copper, aluminium, iron, glass, and plastic are pushed through holes in the side of a metal tank after they have been coated in wax by dipping them in molten candle wax. If water is put into the tank to just below the level of the rods and then brought to the boil, the rods will be warmed by steam and heat will be conducted along the rods. You will find that the wax on the copper will melt first and the molten wax will extend almost to the end of the rod. The distance along the aluminium and iron rods that the wax melts will be shorter than on the copper, and the wax will hardly melt at all on the two non-metallic rods. This indicates that different materials conduct heat to a different extent.

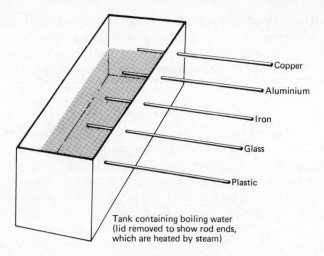

Fig. B10 An experiment to illustrate the differences in conduction of heat by different materials

There is an important property of materials that tells us how good a conductor of heat a material is. This property is known as the *thermal conductivity* of the material and is measured in watts per metre per degree Celsius (W/m °C). The thermal conductivity of some common materials is given in Table B2

Substance	Thermal conductivity (W/m °C)
Aluminium	217.7
Copper	386.5
Iron	79.56
Lead	34.75
Mercury	8.37
Gold	296.1
Oxygen	0.025

Table B2 Thermal conductivities of some common substances

A substance that does not conduct heat readily (e.g. air) is called an *insulator*, and it is possible to group common materials under the headings 'good conductors', 'poor conductors', 'insulators'. Some examples are given on page 61. From these examples it can be seen that metals are very much better conductors of heat than non-metals, and for this reason metals are used in applications where heat has to be transferred by conduction. In those cases where heat losses due to conduction are to be kept as low as possible, non-metals are used.

Good conductors	Poor conductors	Insulators
All metals	Concrete	Wood
	Stone	Slag wool
	Brick	Paper
	Glass	Air
	Water	Cork
		Felt
		Asbestos
		Expanded plastics

Gases are poor conductors of heat, and consequently porous materials which contain large amounts of air which is not free to convect (e.g. slag wool, porous brick, expanded polystyrene) are used to reduce heat losses.

Convection is used to transfer heat in most space-heating systems. In central-heating systems, the boiler is located at the lowest point of the system so that when the water heats up it will rise as its density falls and cold water will move into its place (fig. B11). In this way the water will circulate around the system. When a radiator in a room heats the air around it, the hot air rises and cold air moves in to take its place, thereby causing the whole room to heat up (fig. B12).

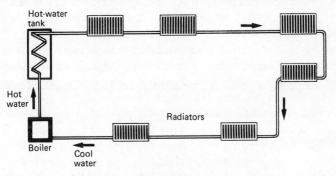

Fig. B11 Layout of a central-heating system

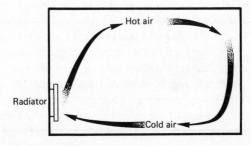

Fig. B12 Heating a room by convection

Radiation is used in industrial furnaces, cooker grills, infra-red space heaters, and electric radiant fires to transfer heat from its source to the article or articles to be heated. The thermal radiation travels in straight lines from the heat source and obeys the same laws as does light (see section 21), so it can be reflected by polished surfaces, as in electric fires with polished reflectors. As the temperature of the radiant body is increased, it will eventually start to emit light as well as heat and will appear red and then white hot.

The amount of heat falling on a body near a source of radiant heat depends on the temperature of the radiator and the distance between the source and the body.

7.3 Uses of insulation to prevent heat loss

A given amount of a fuel, if it is burnt efficiently, will always produce the same amount of heat. It is important that this heat is used in the location where it is required if the fuel is to be used economically. We are all aware of the fact that heat will be lost, and consequently more fuel will have to be burnt, if doors and windows are left open in a house. Just as a room or a house can be heated by conduction and convection, so can large amounts of heat be lost by the same processes, so it is important to ensure in the design that these effects are minimized. We have already seen that some substances are extremely poor conductors, particularly those that contain large amounts of air in an arrangement that prevents the air from convecting. In a central-heating system, the following steps can be taken to minimize unwanted heat losses.

As convection causes the hot air to rise, the majority of heat losses occur through the roof of a house and it is important that the roof space is efficiently insulated. This is achieved either by laying slag wool or fibre-glass between the wooden joists or by using granulated plastics or other insulating materials in these spaces. The hot-water storage tank, which is normally of copper (an excellent conductor of heat), should be lagged to prevent conduction of heat to the surrounding air. If there are spaces under doors and windows, convection causes hot air to rise and cold air will be drawn in through these spaces to replace it, so efficient sealing against draughts is important. Although glass is a poor conductor of heat, in the thicknesses that are commonly used in windows substantial heat losses can occur through normal windows. These heat losses can be greatly reduced by double-glazing, in which two sheets of glass with an air space between them are used. The air, which is a good insulator, prevents heat from being conducted away. The size of the space between the glass is important, however, as convection currents can occur in it if it is too large and heat will be carried across the space by these.

Exercise B6

1. Describe the three methods by which heat may be transferred from a hot body to a colder one.
2. Describe an experiment to compare the thermal conductivities of different metals.
3. In each of the following cases you would feel heat being transmitted to your body. Explain the mechanism of heat transfer in each case.
   (a) Standing in front of an electric fire.
   (b) Sitting in a room containing a central-heating radiator.
   (c) Standing in the sunshine.
   (d) Sitting in a bath of warm water.
   (e) Sitting in a room with an electric fan heater.
   (f) Sitting directly in front of a coal fire.
   (g) Sitting in a room with a coal fire that is shielded from you by furniture.
4. Sketch a domestic heating system and show the transfer of heat in the water and the air in the rooms that it heats.
5. If you were designing a new house, list all the precautions you would take to ensure that the heat produced by the fuel that is burnt in the heating system is used to maximum effect.

8 Effects of heat

8.1 The effect of heat on physical dimensions

Most substances expand when they are heated. We have already seen that temperature measurement in a thermometer depends on the expansion and contraction of mercury or alcohol due to the changes in temperature. Not all substances are affected to the same degree by change in temperature. Brass, for example, expands almost twice as much as steel for a given temperature rise. With solid materials, the expansion due to temperature is compared by using the *coefficient of linear expansion*, which is usually denoted by the Greek letter α (*'alpha'*).

The coefficient of linear expansion of a solid is the increase in length per unit length per 1 °C rise in temperature, or, in symbols,

$$\alpha = \frac{l - l_0}{l_0 t}$$

where l_0 is the original length,

   l is the length to which it expands,

   t is the rise in temperature producing this expansion.

Values of α for common engineering materials are as follows:

| mild steel | $11 \times 10^{-6}/°C$ | brass | $20 \times 10^{-6}/°C$ |
| copper | $17 \times 10^{-6}/°C$ | aluminium | $23 \times 10^{-6}/°C$ |

With liquids and gases the increase in volume is of more significance, and the *coefficient of cubic expansion* is used to compare different liquids and gases. This may be defined as the amount by which unit volume of a material increases for one degree rise in temperature. With gases, the pressure of the gas is also an important variable and the relationship between the pressure, volume, and temperature must be examined.

8.2 Applications and implications of the effect of heat on physical dimensions
The fact that a metal rod will expand as it heats up is the basis of simple thermostats. Figure B13 shows the temperature-control mechanism of an electric frying pan. As the temperature rises, the aluminium rod expands and eventually pushes the electrical contacts A and B apart, thereby switching off the electricity supply to the heating element. As this cools down, the rod contracts and the spring-steel contact arm returns to its original position, bringing A and B together and completing the circuit.

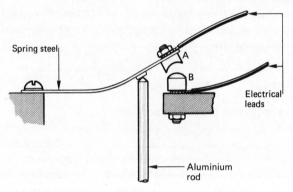

Fig. B13 Control mechanism of an electric frying pan

Another temperature-measuring or -controlling device uses the difference in expansion of different materials. If a brass strip and a steel strip are fixed as shown in fig. B14, when they are cold the contacts X and Y are apart and no current flows. As the temperature rises, the brass expands almost twice as much as the steel and causes the strip to bend as shown, completing an electric circuit which can switch on a warning system. This can be used as the basis for a fire alarm.

The coefficients of expansion of non-metals are normally very low, so the effects of temperature on the dimensions of non-metals can usually be ignored when they are used in situations where the temperature varies. With metals, however, allowances have to be made for the changes in dimensions that can occur when the temperature rises. For example, if we consider a steam-raising plant that can have 100 metres of continuous steel pipe in its construction and

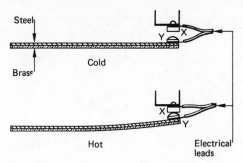

Fig. B14 Bimetal strip used as a temperature-sensing device

an operating temperature of 600 °C, when its temperature rises from cold (say 10 °C) to the operating temperature the pipework will expand. The resulting expansion can be calculated from the formula for the coefficient of linear expansion:

$$\alpha = \frac{l - l_0}{l_0 t}$$

$$11 \times 10^{-6}/°C = \frac{(l - 100)\,\text{m}}{100\,\text{m} \times (600 - 10)\,°C}$$

$$l - 100 = 11 \times 10^{-6} \times 100 \times 590$$

$$= 1.309$$

$$\therefore \qquad l = 101.309$$

This means that the original 100 m of pipework will expand by 1.309 metres and, unless this is allowed for in the design of the plant, considerable damage can result. For this reason also, gaps used to be left between lengths of railway rails to allow for linear expansion.

Expansion of solids can, on the other hand, be used to advantage in engineering practice, as steel collars are frequently fitted to shafts by first heating them so that they expand, fitting them in position, and then cooling them so that the contraction holds them firmly in place.

In order to understand more fully the implications of thermal expansion and contraction, we will work through some examples.

Example 1   A rod is 3.2500 m long at 20 °C and 3.2536 m long at 100 °C. Calculate its coefficient of linear expansion.

$$\text{Coefficient of linear expansion} = \frac{l - l_0}{l_0 t}$$

$$= \frac{(3.2536 - 3.2500) \text{ m}}{3.2500 \text{ m} \times 80\,^{\circ}\text{C}}$$

$$= \frac{0.0036}{260} \,/^{\circ}\text{C}$$

$$= \frac{36 \times 10^{-4}}{2.6 \times 10^2} = 13.85 \times 10^{-6}/^{\circ}\text{C}$$

i.e. the coefficient of linear expansion of the rod material is $13.85 \times 10^{-6}/^{\circ}\text{C}$.

Example 2   An aluminium cable is 100 m long at $0\,^{\circ}\text{C}$. By how much will it expand when its temperature rises from $0\,^{\circ}\text{C}$ to $25\,^{\circ}\text{C}$?

$$23 \times 10^{-6}/^{\circ}\text{C} = \frac{(l - 100) \text{ m}}{100 \text{ m} \times 25\,^{\circ}\text{C}}$$

$$l - 100 = 23 \times 10^{-6} \times 100 \times 25$$

$$= 0.0575$$

$$\therefore \qquad l = 100.0575$$

i.e. the cable will increase in length by 0.0575 m.

Exercise B7
1. A metal rod is 2 m long at $0\,^{\circ}\text{C}$ and 2.002 m long at $100\,^{\circ}\text{C}$. Calculate the coefficient of linear expansion of the metal.
2. A brass metre rule is accurate at $5\,^{\circ}\text{C}$. How inaccurate will a metre measured by it be at $50\,^{\circ}\text{C}$?
3. The length of span of an aluminium power line is 150 m at $20\,^{\circ}\text{C}$. By how much will it contract when the temperature falls to $-10\,^{\circ}\text{C}$?
4. A steel railway line is 100 km long. Calculate the total width of the gaps between the lengths of rails necessary at $0\,^{\circ}\text{C}$ to avoid distortion of the line when the temperature rises from $0\,^{\circ}\text{C}$ to $30\,^{\circ}\text{C}$.

C   Waves

9 Waves and their behaviour

All of us are familiar with the waves that occur on water, ranging from the ripples that we see when rain falls into puddles to the great waves, 20 m high, that can occur in a storm at sea. There are many other forms of waves that are encountered in science, both visible and invisible, so an understanding of the forms that waves can take and their properties is important.

9.1 Examples of waves

We have said that there are many different instances where waves occur. These can conveniently be divided into two main groups: those waves which require a gaseous or liquid medium such as air or water in order to move and those which can travel in the absence of any medium (conditions which can occur in the vacuum of space).

An example of the first kind are the waves that occur in water if it is subject to a vibration. One important property of waves can be seen by studying water, the surface of which has waves on it. If a light object, a cork for example, is floating on water in a container and waves are produced by hitting the side of the container, the cork will move up and down as the waves pass under it but it will have no side-to-side movement unless it is blown across the surface. This indicates that the water is not moving in any direction other than up and down. The waves are in fact energy that is being transmitted through the water with no net movement of the water.

Visible waves being transmitted by a medium can also be studied by using a long cord fastened at one end to a wall, with coloured tape attached to it at intervals. If the free end of the cord is jerked up and down, a wave will be seen travelling from one end of the cord to the other. As it does so, the tapes will move up and down, showing that energy is moving along the cord. The tapes, however, remain in the same position relative to the ground, showing that the energy moves along the medium (in this case the cord) but the material that makes up the medium remains in the same position relative to the horizontal plane, even though it vibrates through this plane.

With all waves, whether visible or not, it is important to distinguish between the vibrations which produce the wave and the wave itself, which is the energy travelling along the medium.

Sound travels by wave motion and needs a medium which can be either a gas such as air or a liquid such as water.

There are other waves that do not require a medium, e.g. the rays of the sun, which travel across the vacuum of space. The rays of the sun give us heat, light, and also produce changes in our skin colour and other chemical effects. These effects are due to waves known as infra-red rays, light rays, and ultra-violet rays respectively.

Radio and television programmes are transmitted as waves which require no medium.

9.2 Wavelength, frequency, and velocity of waves

Although the waves described in section 9.1 are widely different in character, they have certain characteristics that are common to all of them, and indeed to all waves. If we could take a photograph of the surface of water with ripples moving on it, or of the cord as it was being jerked up and down, it would look like fig. C1. If we measure the distance between the similar points on successive waves we get what is known as the wavelength, which is indicated by the Greek letter λ (*lambda*). In this case we have taken the troughs or lowest parts, but we could equally well have taken the crests or highest parts.

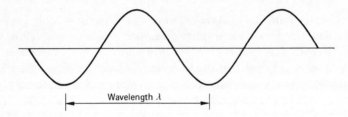

Wavelength λ

Fig. C1 Wavelength

The *wavelength* is defined as *the distance between successive crests or successive troughs of the wave.*

These crests and troughs move along the cord or the surface of the water and if, by careful observation, we could count the number of crests or troughs that passed a fixed point in a given time, we should arrive at what is known as the frequency of the wave.

The *frequency* is defined as *the number of waves passing a given point in one second* and is indicated by the letter f.

Frequency is measured as the number of cycles per second, a cycle being one complete wave. In recognition of the discovery of radio waves by Heinrich Hertz in 1888, 1 cycle per second has been called 1 hertz in SI units, so

68

1 cycle per second (1/s) = 1 hertz (Hz)

10^3 cycles per second = 1 kilohertz (kHz)

10^6 cycles per second = 1 megahertz (MHz)

Broadcasting stations transmit radio waves, and stations are identified by either the wavelength or the frequency of the waves that they transmit. The British Broadcasting Corporation transmits Radio 1 programmes with a wavelength of 247 m and Radio 3 programmes with a wavelength of 464 m. Liverpool's Radio City programmes are transmitted with a frequency of 96.7 MHz, and BBC World Service transmissions have frequencies between 13.82 and 75.90 MHz.

9.3 Velocity of waves

The frequency and the wavelength of waves are related. This can be seen by taking the example of the cord again. If the end is jerked up and down more rapidly, the waves become shorter in length as the frequency increases. If we slow down the movement of the end of the cord, the wavelength increases and the frequency decreases. If we know λ, the length of a wave, and f, the frequency or number of waves that pass a given point in a second, it is possible to calculate the velocity with which the waves are moving past that point. For example, if 2.5 waves pass the fixed point in 1 second and the waves are 2 m long, then $2.5 \times 2 = 5$ m have been travelled by the wave in 1 second so its velocity is 5 m/s. We are determining the velocity of the waves by multiplying together the frequency and the wavelength. If we call the velocity v, we can say that

$$v = f\lambda$$

This is a very important formula, and we shall now look at some examples using it.

Example 1 If a radio broadcast is transmitted at a frequency of 0.2 MHz and a wavelength of 1500 m, calculate the velocity of radio waves.

$v = f\lambda$

$= 0.2 \times 10^6$ Hz $\times 1.5 \times 10^3$ m

$= 3 \times 10^8$ m/s

i.e. the velocity of radio waves is 3×10^8 m/s.

Example 2 Calculate the frequency of radio waves that are transmitted with a wavelength of 247 m if their velocity is 3×10^8 m/s.

$$v = f\lambda$$

$$f = \frac{v}{\lambda}$$

$$= \frac{3 \times 10^8 \, \text{m/s}}{247 \, \text{m}} = 1.22 \times 10^6 \, \text{Hz}$$

$$= 1.22 \, \text{MHz}$$

i.e. the frequency of radio waves of wavelength 247 m is 1.22 MHz.

Example 3 A bass singer sings a note with a frequncy of 256 Hz. If the velocity of sound in air is 340 m/s, calculate the wavelength of this note.

$$v = f\lambda$$

$$\lambda = \frac{v}{f}$$

$$= \frac{340 \, \text{m/s}}{256 \, \text{Hz}} = 1.33 \, \text{m}$$

i.e. the wavelength of the note is 1.33 m.

9.4 Reflection and refraction

A property that all waves have in common is that, when they meet a surface through which they cannot pass, they bounce off it or are *reflected* by it. Light waves are reflected by a mirror. Echoes are sound waves heard after being reflected by a solid surface. The echo of sound which is transmitted by a boat and reflected by the sea bed is used to measure the depth of the sea. Television waves are reflected by satellites kilometres above the Earth, so that programmes from the other side of the Earth's curvature may be received. Waves in the sea are reflected by the sea wall.

The reflection of waves can be studied in a variety of ways. One of the simplest is by using a water tank, the water in which is made to produce waves by a vibrating rod. If a flat surface such as a sheet of glass is placed in the tank at right angles to the water's surface, it is possible to observe the water waves or ripples being reflected from it. Reflection of light waves may be studied by using a mirror and a light source which produces a narrow beam of light directed into the mirror from various positions. We shall look at this in more detail in section 21.

Refraction is the apparent bending or displacement of waves caused by their passing from one medium to another of different density, for example from air to water or from air to glass. All waves refract, but the refraction of light waves is more easily investigated than refraction of other types of wave. We shall also look at refraction in detail in section 21.

70

9.5 Sound waves

If it were possible to 'freeze' a sound wave travelling through air for an instant and take a snapshot of it, we should see a wave made up of layers of air that are alternately denser and less dense. To put it another way, there would be alternate layers of air at a pressure slightly higher than atmospheric pressure (called compressions) and slightly lower than atmospheric (called rarefactions). This idea is shown in fig. C2(a), which shows undisturbed layers of air. When a sound wave passes, there are local changes in pressure as in fig. C2(b) and we can see alternate compressions and rarefactions. This is a different kind of wave from the sort that occurs in water.

Waves in water are examples of *transverse* waves. The sound wave illustrated in fig. C2 is called a *longitudinal* wave. Its wavelength λ is the distance between successive rarefactions. We can consider sound as a pressure wave generated by a source which causes the air around it alternately to compress and expand at a frequency which depends on the type of sound. This pressure wave then travels until the receiver, which may be an ear or a microphone, picks it up.

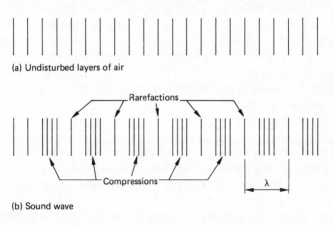

(a) Undisturbed layers of air

Rarefactions

Compressions

λ

(b) Sound wave

Fig. C2 Compressions and rarefactions in a sound wave

Although sound is a longitudinal wave, it can be reflected and refracted in the same way as a transverse wave. As we have already said, echo sounding depends on the ability of sound to be reflected by the bottom of the sea.

9.6 Velocity of sound

The velocity of sound is below that of light. This is easily observed during a thunderstorm, when the time lag between a flash of lightning and the thunder produced by the flash is quite apparent. As you get further away from an echoing surface, the time taken for the echo to reach your ears increases. Echoes were used to estimate the velocity of sound, by measuring the time taken for sound to travel from the observer to a reflecting surface and back again.

The velocity of sound in air is about 340 metres per second or 1224 km/h and depends on the atmospheric pressure and the temperature. Sound travels in water at over four times its velocity in air, its velocity in water being about 1450 m/s or 5200 km/h.

9.7 Generation of sound

We have already said that sound is produced by vibration. Musical instruments produce sound in a variety of ways. In stringed instruments such as violins or guitars, a vibrating string or strings causes the air to vibrate and produces a sound. Wind instruments produce sounds due to the vibrations of columns of air, which may be set in motion by the lips, as in trumpets and other brass instruments, or by reeds, as in clarinets and saxophones. A tuning fork produces a sound due to the vibration of the metal prongs.

In order to produce different notes, the size of the vibrating string or air column is varied. The valves in a trumpet or the slide in a trombone are used to lengthen or shorten the air column. The fingers alter the length of the strings on a guitar, and keys alter the length of the air column in a clarinet. As the vibrating sound generator is made smaller, the sound becomes higher — a tuning fork with short prongs will produce a higher note than one with longer prongs. This indicates that the frequency of vibration is increasing and the wavelength of the vibration is decreasing. In general, the higher the note, the higher the frequency of the vibration.

Exercise C1

1. A radio broadcast is transmitted at a frequency of 96.7 MHz. What is the wavelength of the broadcast if the radio waves travel at 3×10^8 m/s?
2. Explain what are meant by the terms 'frequency' and 'wavelength'. What is the relationship between them?
3. If a note emitted by a piano has a frequency of 256 Hz and a wavelength of 1.33 m, calculate the velocity of sound in air.
4. The time between an observer seeing a flash of lightning and hearing the sound of the thunder it produced was 20 seconds. If you assume that the light from the lightning required no time to reach the observer, calculate how far away the storm was. Assume the speed of sound is 1224 km/h.

D   Electricity

10 Electrical circuits

The existence of electricity has been accepted for over 2500 years, but it was
not until about 1800, when an Italian scientist called Alessandrino Volta in-
vented the *cell*, that the movement of electricity in the form of electric current
could be studied. The usefulness of electricity depends on its flowing in a circuit
as an electric current, and we shall examine the properties of electric currents
in some detail.

10.1 The ampere
A substance through which electricity passes is known as a conductor and it
may be a solid, a liquid, or a gas. The electric current is carried through a conductor by the movement of very small particles, each carrying a small *charge* or
quantity of electricity. The electric current in a circuit is the rate at which
electricity flows past any given point in the circuit. The unit of current is the
ampere, abbreviation A. This unit is named after A. M. Ampère (1775–1836),
a French scientist, and is one of the six SI base units. One ampere represents a
fairly large electric current, so for applications where much smaller currents
flow, for example in transistor radios, smaller units are commonly used:

1 milliampere (mA) = one thousandth of an ampere = 10^{-3} A

1 microampere (μA) = one millionth of an ampere   = 10^{-6} A

10.2 Electrical circuits
In order for an electric current to flow, a complete circuit is necessary. If there
is any discontinuity in the wiring when a battery or other source of electricity
is connected to a light bulb, no electricity will flow and the bulb will not light.
In order to understand the flow of electricity in the form of a current, it is
possible to compare it with the flow of water through a pipe. If we wedge something such as a rubber bung in a pipe through which water is flowing, the flow
stops because we have inserted something in the circuit through which water
cannot flow. Similarly, if we break the wire in an electrical circuit we are in
effect introducing an air gap through which electricity cannot flow and the
current stops.

10.3 Potential difference

If we carry the comparison between electric current and the flow of water a little further, we shall be able to examine the factors that determine the direction in which a current flows. If we have water in a tank at a high pressure and it is connected via a pipe to a tank where the pressure is low, we know that the water will flow from the high-pressure tank to the low-pressure one. The flow of water is due to a pressure difference. If the pressure in the two tanks is the same then the flow will cease.

An electric current flows for a similar reason. If there is a difference in the 'pressure' of electricity at two points in a continuous circuit — usually called a *potential difference* — then electricity will flow between these two points. The greater this potential difference, the more readily will the electricity flow, all other factors being equal.

The unit of potential difference is called the *volt* (abbreviation V), after Volta, and the potential difference is sometimes called the *voltage.*

Electricity is conventionally said to flow from the positive to the negative terminal of an accumulator or battery. Benjamin Franklin, in the eighteenth century, put forward the idea that the positive terminal was at a higher electrical potential than the negative.

10.4 Measurement of current and potential difference

The magnitude of an electric current, or the number of amperes flowing in a circuit, is measured using an instrument known as an *ammeter.* If currents of milliamperes are to be measured, a more sensitive instrument called a *milliammeter* is used, and for currents of microamperes a *microammeter* is used. The principle on which most of these operate is discussed in section 13.5.

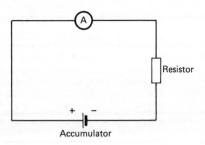

Fig. D1 Use of an ammeter to measure current

In order to measure current, the circuit which is shown in fig. D1 is used. This diagram illustrates some of the symbols that are used to represent electrical components. It is not normal practice to name these components or to mark positive and negative signs on the accumulator. It can be seen from this diagram

74

that the electric current will flow through the ammeter. In this circuit, the ammeter is said to be *in series* with the resistor.

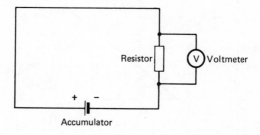

Fig. D2 Use of a voltmeter to measure potential difference (voltage)

Figure D2 shows a voltmeter being used to measure the potential difference across a resistor. Since it measures the difference in potential between two points, it must be connected as shown in the diagram — this arrangement is called *in parallel*.

The difference in the ways that ammeters and voltmeters are connected in a circuit is due to the fact that ammeters are used to measure current and the current must be allowed to flow through them. Voltmeters on the other hand measure the potential difference between two points and so are connected in parallel across the points. All the current flows through the ammeter, so it must have a low resistance to electricity. In order to stop a significant amount of electricity flowing through it, a voltmeter must itself have a very high resistance to the flow of electricity so that practically all the electricity flows through the main circuit.

10.5 Relationship between potential difference and current
In 1827, G. S. Ohm investigated the relationship between potential difference and current. In order to carry out a similar investigation we need to set up a circuit as shown in fig. D3. If the variable resistor is adjusted to give different

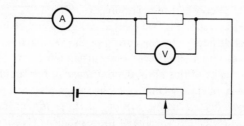

Fig. D3 Circuit to study variation of potential difference with current

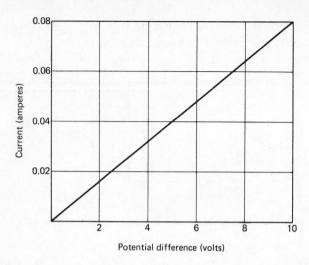

Fig. D4 Relationship between current and potential difference for a single resistor

currents measured on ammeter A, and the potential difference across the fixed resistor is measured on voltmeter V, a graph of current against potential difference as shown in fig. D4 will be obtained. This shows a straight line, which means that the ratio of potential difference to current remains constant. This relationship is an expression of *Ohm's law*, which can be stated fully as follows:

> *the electric current flowing in a given conductor is directly proportional to the potential difference applied, provided that the temperature of the conductor remains constant.*

If, however, the temperature of the resistor varies, as would happen if we used a light bulb in place of a conventional resistor, a graph of current against potential difference would look like fig. D5, showing that the ratio of potential difference to current was not constant. This is due to the temperature of the light-bulb filament rising and causing the resistance to vary. However, resistance should be constant at constant temperature.

If we examine the results that we plotted in fig. D4 and divide the different values of potential difference by the corresponding currents, we find that the value of the ratio of potential difference to current always works out to 125.

Ohm called the value of this ratio, the *resistance* of the circuit. This then gives us another way of stating Ohm's law, by saying that, *in a given circuit, the potential difference divided by the current is equal to the resistance.* We have already seen that the greater the value of the resistance of a circuit, the more difficult it is for a current to flow under a given potential difference.

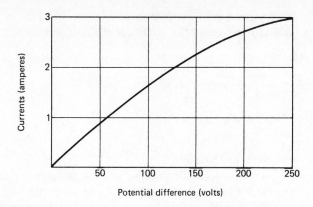

Fig. D5 Relationship between current and potential difference for a 'non-linear' conductor

To acknowledge Ohm's work in this subject, the units of resistance were called ohms, so in the circuit above, where a potential difference of 10 volts produces a current of 0.08 amperes, we can say that the resistance is

$$\frac{10 \text{ V}}{0.08 \text{ A}} = 125 \text{ ohms } (\Omega)$$

(The Greek letter *omega* is used as the abbreviation for ohms, in order to avoid confusion with zero.)

If we call the current I, the potential difference V, and the resistance R, we can express Ohm's law as

$$\frac{V}{I} = R \quad \text{or} \quad V = IR$$

10.6 Problems
The simple expression of Ohm's law, $V = IR$, may be used to solve problems as follows.

Example 1 The current flowing through a resistor is 0.05 A when a potential difference of 10 V is applied. What is the value of the resistance?

$$V = IR$$

$$R = \frac{V}{I} = \frac{10 \text{ V}}{0.05 \text{ A}} = 200 \; \Omega$$

i.e. the resistance is 200 ohms.

Example 2   What current will flow through the filament of a light bulb whose resistance is 1000 Ω when a potential difference of 250 V is applied to it.

$$V = IR$$

$$I = \frac{V}{R} = \frac{250 \text{ V}}{1000 \text{ }\Omega} = 0.25 \text{ A}$$

i.e. a current of 0.25 A will flow.

10.7 Resistors in series and parallel

Figure D6 shows an electrical circuit containing an accumulator, a variable resistor, an ammeter to measure the current flowing in the circuit, and three fixed resistors R_1, R_2, R_3 with a voltmeter connected across them so that the potential difference across these resistors may be measured. The arrangement of the three resistors R_1, R_2, R_3 is called a *series* arrangement. This is because they are connected one after the other so that the current passes in turn through all three of them.

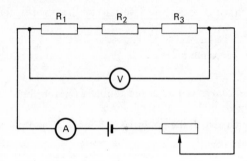

Fig. D6 Resistors arranged in series

Figure D7 shows a circuit that is connected similarly except that the three resistors are arranged in *parallel*. This means that in this case the current divides so that parts of it pass through each of the three resistors.

10.8 Current in a series circuit

In the circuit shown in fig. D6, the size of the current that flows is measured by the ammeter A. The value of this current will be the same wherever the ammeter is located, unless it is connected in that part of the circuit in which the voltmeter V is connected. So we can say that

> *the current flowing is the same in all the parts of the circuit which are connected in series.*

78

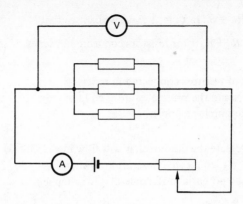

Fig. D7 Resistors arranged in parallel

10.9 Voltages in a series circuit

Still considering the circuit in fig. D6, if the values of the resistors were R_1 = 8 Ω, R_2 = 5 Ω, R_3 = 2 Ω, and if we were to set the variable resistance so that, for example, a current of 1 A flowed in the circuit, we should find that across R_1 the potential difference V_1 would be given by Ohm's law:

$$V_1 = IR = 1\,\text{A} \times 8\,\Omega = 8\,\text{V}$$

Across R_2,

$$V_2 = 1\,\text{A} \times 5\,\Omega = 5\,\text{V}$$

Across R_3,

$$V_3 = 1\,\text{A} \times 2\,\Omega = 2\,\text{V}$$

If we measured the voltage across all three resistors together by using the arrangement shown in fig. D6, we should find that the potential difference would be 15 V. This experiment illustrates the fact that the sum of the voltages in a series circuit is equal to the total applied voltage.

10.10 Value of resistors in series

Using the example in section 10.9, and applying Ohm's law, if the total potential difference is 15 V and the current flowing is 1 A then the total resistance R of the circuit is given by

$$R = \frac{V}{I} = \frac{15\,\text{V}}{1\,\text{A}} = 15\,\Omega$$

but $R_1 = 8\,\Omega, R_2 = 5\,\Omega, R_3 = 2\,\Omega$, so we can see that

$$R = R_1 + R_2 + R_3 \quad \text{for resistors connected in series.}$$

10.11 Examples of resistors connected in series

In order to understand the principles outlined in sections 10.9 and 10.10, we shall look at some simple examples.

Example 1   Calculate the current that will flow in a circuit which has three resistors, R_1, R_2, R_3, connected in series in it when $R_1 = 50\,\Omega, R_2 = 75\,\Omega$, $R_3 = 125\,\Omega$ and a potential difference of 1 V is applied.

$$R = R_1 + R_2 + R_3$$

$$= 50\,\Omega + 75\,\Omega + 125\,\Omega$$

$$= 250\,\Omega$$

$$I = \frac{V}{R}$$

$$= \frac{1\,\text{V}}{250\,\Omega} = 4 \times 10^{-3}\,\text{A}$$

$$= 4\,\text{mA}$$

i.e. a current of 4 mA will flow.

Example 2   An electrical circuit contains two resistors R_1 and R_2 in series. The resistance of R_1 is 100 Ω. When a current of 0.5 A flows in the circuit, the potential difference across the two resistors is 60 V. What is the resistance of R_2?

$$R = \frac{V}{I}$$

$$= \frac{60\,\text{V}}{0.5\,\text{A}}$$

$$= 120\,\Omega$$

But $R = R_1 + R_2$, and $R_1 = 100\,\Omega$, so

$$R_2 = 120\,\Omega - 100\,\Omega = 20\,\Omega$$

i.e. the resistance of R_2 is 20 ohms.

Example 3   A circuit contains three resistors in series. Their resistances R_1, R_2, and R_3 are such that $R_1 = R_2 + R_3$ and $R_2 = 4R_3$. When a potential difference of 50 V is applied to the circuit, a current of 1 mA flows in it. Calculate the resistances of the three resistors.

$$R = \frac{V}{I}$$

$$= \frac{50\,V}{1 \times 10^{-3}\,A} = 50\,k\Omega$$

$R = R_1 + R_2 + R_3$, but $R_1 = R_2 + R_3$, therefore

$$R = R_1 + R_1$$

or $50\,k\Omega = 2R_1$

$$R_1 = 25\,k\Omega$$

$$R_2 + R_3 = R - 25\,k\Omega$$

$$= 25\,k\Omega$$

But $R_2 = 4R_3$, therefore

$$4R_3 + R_3 = 25\,k\Omega$$

$$R_3 = \frac{25}{5}\,k\Omega = 5\,k\Omega$$

and $R_2 = 20\,k\Omega$

i.e. R_1, R_2, and R_3 have values of 25 kΩ, 20 kΩ, and 5 kΩ respectively.

10.12 Current in parallel circuits

If we look again at the circuit shown in fig. D7 in which there are three resistors arranged in parallel, we can see what will happen to the current flowing in this circuit. When the current reaches the point at which the three resistors are connected in parallel to the positive terminal of the accumulator, it will divide and some of the electricity will pass through each of the three resistors. More will pass through the resistor with the lowest resistance and the least will pass through the one with the highest resistance.

When the current which has been passing through the resistors reaches the point where they are connected to the negative pole of the accumulator, all the current will again flow through the single connecting wire. It can be seen, then, that the same amount of current enters and leaves the combination of resistors and this is equal to the total current flowing in the circuit. We can say, therefore, that

> *the sum of the current flowing in resistors connected in parallel is equal to the current flowing in the rest of the circuit.*

10.13 Potential difference across resistors in parallel

As the three resistors in fig. D7 are connected to the same two points in the circuit, if the potential difference is measured across these two points by the voltmeter V, the voltage obtained will be the potential difference across all three resistors. This means that *the potential difference across all the resistors in parallel is the same.*

10.14 Equivalent resistance of three resistors in parallel

Using the two previous sections, 10.12 and 10.13, we can examine the resistance of resistors connected in parallel.

Let us call the resistances of the three resistors connected in parallel R_1, R_2, R_3 and the corresponding currents flowing in them I_1, I_2, I_3. We have said that the potential difference V across the resistors is the same. It follows then, from Ohm's law, that

$$I_1 = \frac{V}{R_1} \qquad I_2 = \frac{V}{R_2} \qquad I_3 = \frac{V}{R_3}$$

The total current flowing, I, is the sum of the current flowing through each of the resistors:

$$I = \frac{V}{R_1} + \frac{V}{R_2} + \frac{V}{R_3}$$

But, from Ohm's law

$$I = \frac{V}{R} \quad \text{where } R \text{ is the total resistance}$$

so we can say

$$\frac{V}{R} = \frac{V}{R_1} + \frac{V}{R_2} + \frac{V}{R_3}$$

If we divide both sides of this expression by V, it becomes

$$\frac{1}{R} = \frac{1}{R_1} + \frac{1}{R_2} + \frac{1}{R_3}$$

This is an important relationship and it gives a way of calculating the total resistance in a circuit when the resistances of resistors connected in parallel are known.

10.15 Problems involving resistors connected in parallel

In order to illustrate how the relationship for parallel resistors

$$\frac{1}{R} = \frac{1}{R_1} + \frac{1}{R_2} + \frac{1}{R_3}$$

may be used, we shall work through some examples.

Example 1   Two resistors, whose resistances are $100 \ \Omega$ and $400 \ \Omega$, are connected in parallel in a circuit. Calculate the total resistance of the circuit.

What current will flow (a) in the circuit, (b) in each resistor if a potential difference of 40 V is applied?

$$\frac{1}{R} = \frac{1}{R_1} + \frac{1}{R_2}$$

$$= \frac{1}{100 \ \Omega} + \frac{1}{400 \ \Omega}$$

$$= \frac{4+1}{400 \ \Omega}$$

$$= \frac{5}{400 \ \Omega}$$

$$\therefore \quad R = \frac{400 \ \Omega}{5} = 80 \ \Omega$$

i.e. the total resistance of the circuit is $80 \ \Omega$.

Total current:

$$I = \frac{V}{R}$$

$$= \frac{40 \ V}{80 \ \Omega} = 0.5 \ A$$

i.e. a total current of 0.5 A flows in the circuit.

Current in the $100 \ \Omega$ resistor (R_1):

$$I_1 = \frac{V}{R_1}$$

$$= \frac{40 \ V}{100 \ \Omega} = 0.4 \ A$$

Current in the $400 \ \Omega$ resistor (R_2):

$$I_2 = \frac{V}{R_2}$$

$$= \frac{40 \ V}{100 \ \Omega} = 0.1 \ A$$

i.e. a current of 0.4 A flows in the $100 \ \Omega$ resistor and of 0.1 A in the $400 \ \Omega$ resistor.

Example 2   Three resistors of equal resistance are connected in parallel in a circuit. When a potential difference of 1.5 V is applied across these resistors, a current of 0.15 A flows in the circuit. Calculate the resistance of the resistors.

Total resistance $R = \dfrac{V}{I}$

$$= \frac{1.5 \text{ V}}{0.15 \text{ A}} = 10 \text{ }\Omega$$

$$\frac{1}{R} = \frac{1}{R_1} + \frac{1}{R_2} + \frac{1}{R_3}$$

but $R_1 = R_2 = R_3$,

$$\therefore \quad \frac{1}{10 \text{ }\Omega} = \frac{3}{R_1}$$

$$R_1 = 30 \text{ }\Omega$$

i.e. the resistance of each resistor is 30 Ω.

Example 3   Three resistors, of resistance 250 Ω, 500 Ω, 750 Ω, are connected in parallel in a circuit. Calculate the potential difference that must be applied to cause a current of 0.1 mA to flow in the circuit.

$$\frac{1}{R} = \frac{1}{R_1} + \frac{1}{R_2} + \frac{1}{R_3}$$

$$= \frac{1}{250 \text{ }\Omega} + \frac{1}{500 \text{ }\Omega} + \frac{1}{750 \text{ }\Omega}$$

$$= \frac{6 + 3 + 2}{1500 \text{ }\Omega}$$

$$= \frac{11}{1500 \text{ }\Omega}$$

$$\therefore \quad R = \frac{1500 \text{ }\Omega}{11}$$

$$= 136.4 \text{ }\Omega$$

$$V = IR$$

$$= (1 \times 10^{-4}) \text{ A} \times (1.364 \times 10^2) \text{ }\Omega$$

$$= 1.364 \times 10^{-2} \text{ V}$$

$$= 13.64 \text{ mV}$$

i.e. a potential difference of 13.64 mV must be applied.

10.16 Resistance of a conductor

If different lengths of wire made from a uniform conducting material are connected in turn into a circuit in which a constant potential difference is maintained, it will be found by measuring the current flowing in the circuit and applying Ohm's law that the resistance of the conducting material increases with length. If several pieces of the same length and of the same material but with differing cross-sectional areas are used, it will be found that the resistance will increase as the cross-sectional area becomes smaller. The composition of the material also affects its resistance, and a property known as the *resistivity* of the substance is used to indicate the extent to which a particular material resists the flow of electricity.

If R is the resistance of a length l of a material whose cross-sectional area is a, we can say that R is proportional to l and proportional to $1/a$ and it also depends on a property of the material known as the resistivity (indicated by ρ, the Greek letter *rho*), which is measured in ohm metres (Ω m) and is constant for a given material. Combining all these statements, we arrive at the expression

$$R = \rho \frac{l}{a}$$

Problems using this formula are discussed in section 22.3.

10.17 Resistance and temperature

By measuring the current flowing in a circuit under a fixed potential, it can be shown that, if the temperature of part of the circuit rises, then the current will fall, indicating that the resistance increases as the temperature increases. For a length of copper wire whose resistance at 0 °C is exactly 1 Ω, its resistance at 100 °C would be 1.426 Ω.

10.18 Wiring lamps in series and parallel

If lamps are wired in series, as is sometimes the case with cheaper Christmas-tree lights, the circuit will be broken if one lamp is faulty, and none of the lights will work. However, if one lamp is faulty with parallel wiring, the circuit will still be completed through the sound lamps and the sound lamps will still light.

Also, if a set of ten lights, each with a resistance of 500 Ω, were connected in series, the total resistance of the circuit would be 5000 Ω. If they were connected in parallel, the total resistance would be given by

$$\frac{1}{R} = \frac{1 \times 10}{500 \ \Omega}$$

$$R = 50 \ \Omega$$

so the same current would be produced by a much lower potential difference for the connection in parallel.

Exercise D1

1. State Ohm's law.

    A potential difference of 12 V applied across a resistor caused a current of 0.4 mA to flow in it. What is the resistance of the resistor?

2. An electrical current has three resistors arranged in series. When a potential difference of 100 V is applied across these resistors a current of 0.1 A flows. The resistances of two of the resistors are 10 Ω and 15 Ω. What is the resistance of the third?

3. Calculate the resistance of each of three resistors of equal resistance which, when connected in series with a potential source of 150 V, allow a current of 1 μA to flow.

4. A circuit has three resistors whose resistances are 10 MΩ, 5 MΩ, and 7.5 MΩ connected in series. What potential must be applied to produce a current of 3.75 μA?

5. Two resistors are connected in parallel. They have equal resistances and, when a current of 1 A flows in the circuit, the potential difference across the two resistors is 10 V. What is the resistance of each of the resistors?

6. A circuit has three resistors connected in parallel. If the resistances of the resistors are 10 Ω, 15 Ω, and 24 Ω respectively, what current will flow (a) in the circuit, (b) in the 10 Ω resistor when a potential difference of 12 V exists across the resistors?

7. Three resistors, R_1, R_2, and R_3, are connected in parallel with a potential source of 100 V. R_1 has a resistance of 1 Ω, R_2 a resistance of 3 Ω, and a current of 15 μA flows in the circuit. Calculate the resistance of R_3.

11 Effects of an electric current

When an electric current passes through a circuit, it can have one or more of the following effects:

a) a magnetic effect,
b) a chemical effect,
c) a heating effect

These effects can be used to perform useful tasks, and we shall look at each of them in turn.

11.1 Magnetic effect

The reason why an electric current produces a magnetic effect is outside the scope of this book — we shall concern ourselves only with how this magnetic effect may be used. One of the commonest uses of the magnetic effect of a current is in a large variety of what are known as moving-coil ammeters and voltmeters, where magnetism produced by a current is used to move a pointer over a scale by an amount which corresponds to the size of the current that is passing (see section 13.5).

Magnetism is also used in a variety of ways in industry for lifting magnetic materials such as iron and steel. It is much more convenient to have a lifting device which uses an electromagnet, rather than a permanent magnet, since the current, and consequently the magnetic lifting effect, may be shut off.

The magnetic effect of an electric current, when it is used to produce motion in a coil, forms the basis of electric motors which are used to a vast extent in industrial and domestic applications. Electric bells and loudspeakers also make use of electromagnetic effects.

11.2 Chemical effect

When an electric current is passed through an electrolyte (a liquid that conducts electricity), it causes charged particles, or ions, to move in that electrolyte (see section 19.2). This can be utilized to produce two main effects. *Electrodeposition,* one of the effects, occurs when the current causes metal to be deposited from a solution, either to produce a pure metal from an impure solution, as in *electrorefining,* or to produce a decorative or protective layer on another metal, as in *electroplating.*

Electrolytic dissolution is the other principal chemical effect and is used to cause substances to dissolve in a solution in which they are not normally soluble. This is used in *electrochemical machining,* a process whereby metals that are not easily machined by mechanical means may be shaped by the chemical effect of an electric current.

11.3 Heating effect

When an electric current passes through a material with a high electrical resistance and a low thermal conductivity, it will cause it to heat up. This phenomenon is the basis of electric fires, cookers, and kettles.

The heating effect of electric current is also the basis of fuses which are used to prevent overloading of electrical circuits. A fuse made of a metal with a low melting point is made part of the circuit. If an excessive current flows, the fuse overheats and melts, thereby breaking the circuit.

12 Electrical power

In section 4.9, power was defined as the rate at which work is done, or the rate at which energy is transferred or consumed. Electrical power fulfils this definition.

12.1 Power in a circuit

When a potential difference causes a current to flow in an electrical circuit, the rate at which energy is being consumed is given by the relationship

power = current x potential difference

If the current (I) flowing in a circuit is measured in amperes and the potential difference (V) in volts, the power (P) used by that circuit will be in watts.

An electric fire connected to a 250 V supply in which a current of 4 A flows is using electrical power of

$$4 \text{ A} \times 250 \text{ V} = 1000 \text{ W} \quad \text{or} \quad 1 \text{ kW}$$

Similarly, a 3 kW heating element in an immersion heater operating on a 250 V supply has a current flowing through it of

$$\frac{3000 \text{ W}}{250 \text{ V}} = 12 \text{ A}$$

12.2 Power and resistance of a circuit
We have seen that

$$\text{power} = \text{current} \times \text{potential difference} \quad \text{or} \quad P = IV$$

From Ohm's law we know that $V = IR$ and $I = V/R$ so, if we substitute this value in the power equation,

$$P = IV = I \times IR \quad \text{or} \quad (V/R) \times V$$

or $\quad P = I^2R = V^2/R$

12.3 Calculation of power consumption
In order to illustrate their significance, we shall look at some of the uses of the equations for power given in the previous sections.

Example 1 What is the current flowing through a 60 W bulb operating in a circuit with a voltage of 240 V?

$$P = IV$$

so $\quad I = \dfrac{P}{V} = \dfrac{60 \text{ W}}{240 \text{ V}} = 0.25 \text{ A}$

i.e. a current of 0.25 A is flowing.

Example 2 Calculate the power used by a heater operating in a 110 V system through which 22 A are flowing.

$$P = IV = 22 \text{ A} \times 110 \text{ V} = 2420 \text{ W} = 2.42 \text{ kW}$$

i.e. the power used is 2.42 kW.

Example 3 Calculate the power used by a cooker element whose resistance is 60 Ω when a current of 4 A flows in it.

$$P = I^2R = 4\,A \times 4\,A \times 60\,\Omega = 960\,W$$

i.e. the power used is 960 W.

Example 4   Calculate the resistance of the filament of a 60 W light bulb that is used in a 240 V circuit.

$$P = IV$$

Current flowing:

$$I = \frac{P}{V} = \frac{60\,W}{240\,V} = 0.25\,A$$

Resistance of filament:

$$R = \frac{V}{I} = \frac{240\,V}{0.25\,A} = 960\,\Omega$$

i.e. the resistance of the filament is 960 Ω.

Exercise D2
1. What current flows in a 250 V circuit when a 3 kW heater is running in it?
2. Calculate the power consumed when a potential difference of 10 V is applied to a circuit which has a resistance of 1 mΩ.
3. What is the resistance of a 150 W bulb connected in a 250 V circuit?
4. Two resistors, of values 10 Ω and 20 Ω, are connected in parallel with a potential source of 12 V. Calculate the current flowing and the power consumed (a) in the total circuit and (b) in each resistor.
5. Resistors of resistance 100 Ω, 200 Ω, and 300 Ω are connected in series in a circuit where a current of 1 mA flows. Calculate the power consumed by this circuit.
6. What is the resistance of each of two equal resistors connected in parallel in a circuit where the potential difference is 240 V and the power consumption 1 kW?

13   Magnetic fields and electric current

Various magnetic effects may be observed in the vicinity of any magnet — iron filings and compass needles are noticeably affected by the presence of a permanent magnet or a current flowing in a wire. The region affected by the magnet is known as its *magnetic field*. Magnetic fields are used in all branches of the electrical and electronics industries. Loudspeakers, transformers, motors, generators, television tubes, and tape-recorders are just some of the common appliances that use magnetic fields in their operation.

13.1 Forces in a magnetic field

If a magnet is placed in a magnetic field produced by another magnet, or in a naturally occurring magnetic field, it experiences a force which tends to move it or to change its direction or rate of movement if it is already moving. The simplest use of this phenomenon is the compass needle, which is a light magnet which, under the influence of the Earth's magnetic field, will move until it has aligned itself in a north—south direction. If another magnet is brought near it, it will be apparent that this magnet produces a magnetic field which will cause the compass-needle magnet to move. The end of a magnet which points north under the action of the Earth's magnetic field is called the north pole of the magnet; the other end is called the south pole.

13.2 Magnetic fields around conductors

If a compass needle or a freely suspended magnet is brought near to a conductor carrying a large current, it will experience forces that can cause it to realign itself. This is because the passage of an electric current through a conductor produces a magnetic field. The intensity of this field depends on the magnitude of the current flowing in the conductor and on the shape of the conductor (a coil of wire produces a different type of field from a straight piece of wire).

13.3 Magnetic field patterns

A simple way of examining the pattern of a magnetic field around a magnet is to place the magnet under a sheet of thin glass or paper and to sprinkle this glass or paper with iron filings. The filings will arrange themselves in very definite patterns depending on the type of magnet being used.

A simple bar magnet consisting of a rectangular-section rod of magnetized metal will produce a magnetic field as shown in fig. D8, with *lines of force*, on which the iron filings are concentrated, running from the north pole to the south pole of the magnet.

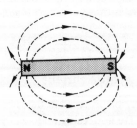

Fig. D8 Magnetic field around a bar magnet

A *solenoid*, which is another name for a coil of wire with a current passing through it, will produce elliptical lines of force as shown in fig. D9.

90

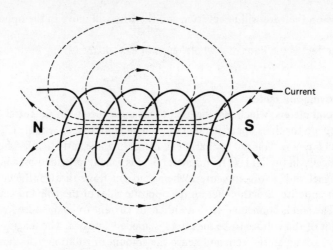

Fig. D9 Magnetic field around a solenoid

13.4 Forces on a conductor in a magnetic field

If a straight length of wire is arranged in a magnetic field such that it is free to move, as shown in fig. D10, when a current is passed through the wire, the wire will move out of the field in the direction shown. This motion must be the result of a force acting on the wire. When the current is switched off, the wire will fall back into the magnetic field. If the direction of the current is reversed,

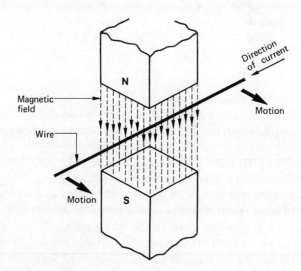

Fig. D10 A current-carrying conductor in a magnetic field

the force on the wire will be reversed and the wire will move in the opposite direction.

This effect is the basis of a whole range of electric measuring devices and motors.

13.5 Moving-coil meters

Moving-coil meters, which may be used to measure current or potential difference, depend for their operation on the principle outlined in section 13.4. A rectangular coil is arranged so that it can rotate in a magnetic field as shown schematically in fig. D11. (The magnetic field is usually provided by a horse-shoe magnet with a soft-iron core.) When a current flows through the coil, forces in opposite directions act on the opposite sides of the coil and cause it to rotate. The coil is connected so that either the current to be measured passes through it or the voltage to be measured is applied across it. The magnitude of the forces acting on the coil, and hence the amount of rotation, will then depend on the magnitude of the current or potential difference. By attaching to the coil a pointer which can move over a calibrated scale, the size of the current or potential difference can be measured.

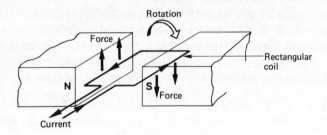

Fig. D11 Principle of the moving-coil meter

13.6 Operation of a direct-current motor

The direct-current electric motor, which is used to power electric trains and many machines in industry, is also based on the principle described in section 13.4.

As shown in fig. D12, it consists of a rectangular coil, called the *armature*, which can rotate about a fixed axis inside a powerful magnetic field produced either by a permanent magnet or, as is more common, by an electromagnet. Current is fed into the coil through a *commutator*, which in its simplest form consists of a split copper ring whose two halves are insulated from each other and which pick up electricity from two carbon *brushes* rubbing on them.

As with the moving-coil meter described in section 13.5, current flowing through the coil produces forces which make the coil rotate. When the coil has

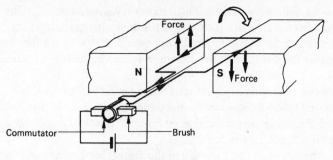

Fig. D12 Principle of the direct-current motor

turned through 90° from the position shown, the brushes connected to the positive and negative terminals of the d.c. supply make contact with different halves of the commutator ring, thus reversing the direction of the current through the coil. The side of the coil which previously experienced an upward force will then experience a downward force, and vice versa, so the coil will continue to rotate — without the commutator the coil would remain at 90° to its original position.

13.7 Movement of a permanent magnet inside a coil

To examine what happens when a permanent magnet is moved inside a coil, we need to use an instrument called a central-zero galvanometer. This is a sensitive ammeter with its zero-current position in the centre of the scale. When current flows through it in one direction, the pointer moves to the right; when current flows in the opposite direction, the pointer moves to the left.

If a coil of wire is connected to a central-zero galvanometer and a permanent magnet is moved into the coil, there will be a deflection of the pointer of the galvanometer (fig. D13(a)). This indicates that an electric current has been pro-

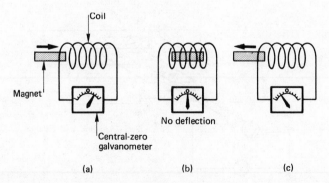

Fig. D13 Relative movement of a coil and a magnet

93

duced in the coil. If the magnet is held stationary within the coil, there will be no deflection (fig. D13(b)). If the magnet is then withdrawn from the coil there will again be a deflection – but in the opposite direction to the first case, indicating that the direction of the current produced in the coil is reversed (fig. D13(c)).

If, instead of moving a magnet towards and away from a stationary coil, a coil is moved towards and away from a stationary magnet, the same effect is produced. From this we can see that relative movement of a coil and a permanent magnet will generate electricity.

If the speed with which the coil and the magnet are brought together or separated is increased, the magnitude of deflection on the galvanometer will be seen to increase – in fact, the magnitude of the current produced in the coil depends on the rate at which the wire of the coil cuts through the lines of force of the magnet.

13.8 Generation of an alternating current
The effect described in section 13.7 is the basis of the type of generator which is used to produce the electric current supplied to domestic and industrial users in most countries.

In its simplest form, this generator consists of a rectangular coil which is rotated at constant speed on a fixed axis inside a magnetic field as shown in fig. D14. As the coil is rotated, each side of the coil cuts through the lines of force of the magnetic field. When the coil is rotating through the position shown in fig. D15(a), the rate at which it cuts the lines of force and hence the current produced in the coil will be a maximum. As the coil rotates through the position shown in fig. D15(b), the rate at which it cuts the lines of force and hence the current produced will be less. At the instant that the coil rotates

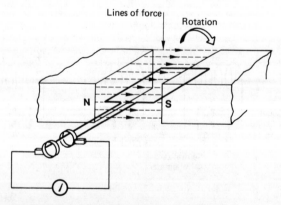

Fig. D14 Principle of the a.c. generator

94

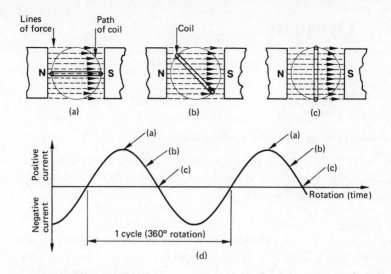

Fig. D15 Alternating current

through the position shown in fig. D15(c) the coil is moving parallel to the lines of force and does not cut through them, so no current is produced.

As the coil continues to rotate, it cuts through the lines of force from the opposite direction and a current in the opposite direction increases in magnitude until the coil has rotated through 180° from the position shown in fig. D15(a), then decreasing to reach zero after a further 90° rotation. The current then builds up in the original direction, reaching a maximum when the coil is back in the position shown in fig. D15(a), after which the cycle is repeated.

The variation of current with rotation (or time) is shown in fig. D15(d). A current such as this, which passes through positive, zero, and negative values, is called an *alternating current.*

The current produced is fed from the coil by brushes rubbing on two copper slip-rings, one attached to each end of the coil.

Exercise D3
1. Explain the basic operation of a moving-coil meter.
2. Explain the basic operation of a d.c. motor.
3. Describe what happens when a permanent magnet is moved in a coil of wire connected to a sensitive galvanometer.
4. Explain the basic operation of an a.c. generator.
5. With the aid of sketches, describe the types of magnetic field produced by
   (a) a bar magnet and (b) a solenoid.

E   Dynamics

14 Uniform motion and acceleration

Dynamics is the branch of engineering science concerned with movement, and in this section we shall look at the forces acting on bodies in motion and examine some properties of moving bodies.

14.1 Speed

If a car travels 30 miles in an hour we say that its speed is 30 miles per hour. If it travels 3 km in 2 minutes we say its speed is 1.5 km per minute or 1.5 x 60 = 90 km per hour, or 1.5 ÷ 60 = 0.025 km per second or 25 m per second (m/s). All the above values are understood to be speeds and they all have one thing in common: they express a distance travelled in a particular unit of time, whether it is metres per second, kilometres per hour, or miles per hour.

Speed can be defined, then, as *the distance travelled in a unit of time* or *the rate at which a distance is traversed*.

Normally when we talk of speed we are implying *average* speed. If a car takes 1 hour to cover 25 km, at some times in the hour it may be stationary and at others travelling at much higher speeds than 25 km/h, but its average speed will be 25 km/h.

Constant speed occurs only if a body moves over equal distances in equal intervals of time, however small.

14.2 Speed calculated from time and distance data

The average speed of a moving body is the total distance it travels in a given time divided by that time. So, if a body travels 60 metres in 10 seconds, the average speed (v) is given by

$$v = \frac{60 \text{ m}}{10 \text{ s}} = 6 \text{ m/s}$$

If it travels 30 km in 2 hours,

$$v = \frac{30 \text{ km}}{2 \text{ h}} = 15 \text{ km/h}$$

In general, if v = average speed, s = distance travelled, and t = time,

$$v = \frac{s}{t} \quad \text{or} \quad s = vt \quad \text{and} \quad t = \frac{s}{v}$$

If we know the average speed of a moving body, we can calculate how far it will travel in a particular time.

Example 1   How far will a car moving at 60 km/h travel in 30 seconds?

Using $s = vt$, where $v = 60$ km/h,

$$v = \frac{60 \times 1000 \text{ m}}{3600 \text{ s}}$$

$$t = 30 \text{ s}$$

$$\therefore \quad s = vt$$

$$= \frac{60 \times 1000 \text{ m}}{3600 \text{ s}} \times 30 \text{ s} = 500 \text{ m}$$

i.e. the car will travel 500 m in 30 seconds.

We can also calculate how long it will take to cover a particular distance given the average speed.

Example 2   An aeroplane travels at 800 km/h. How long will it take to travel a distance of 2500 km?

$$t = \frac{s}{v}$$

$$= \frac{2500 \text{ km}}{800 \text{ km/h}} = \frac{2500 \times 60}{800} \text{ min}$$

$$= 187\tfrac{1}{2} \text{ min} \quad \text{or} \quad 3 \text{ h } 7\tfrac{1}{2} \text{ min}$$

i.e. it will take 3 hours $7\tfrac{1}{2}$ minutes to travel 2500 km.

Example 3   A train takes 2.5 hours to travel 360 km. Calculate (a) its speed in km/h, (b) the distance it covers in 1 second, (c) the time it takes to travel 10 km.

a) $v = \dfrac{s}{t}$

$$v = \frac{360 \text{ km}}{2.5 \text{ h}} = 144 \text{ km/h}$$

i.e. the speed is 144 km/h.

b) If the train covers 144 km in 1 hour, the distance covered in 1 second is

$$\frac{144 \times 10^3}{3600} = 40 \text{ metres}$$

i.e. the train will travel 40 metres in one second.

c) From (a), $v = 144$ km/h

$\therefore$ time to cover 10 km $= \dfrac{s}{v}$

$$= \dfrac{10 \text{ km}}{144 \text{ km/h}}$$

$$= \dfrac{10 \times 60 \times 60}{144} = 250 \text{ s}$$

$$= 4 \text{ min } 10 \text{ s}$$

i.e. the time taken to cover 10 km is 4 minutes 10 seconds.

14.3 Distance–time graphs

The relationship between the distance travelled in a certain time and the time spent in travelling can be represented on graphs which can then be used to obtain some useful information. If we look at some of these graphs plotted for bodies moving at constant speeds, we will see what information can be obtained.

Figure E1 shows the relationship between distance travelled and time taken for an object which travels 10 metres in 5 seconds, 20 metres in 10 seconds, 30 metres in 15 seconds, 40 metres in 20 seconds, and 100 metres in 50 seconds. The graph shows a straight line. This indicates that the speed of the object is constant. In order to calculate the slope of this line we divide the value on the

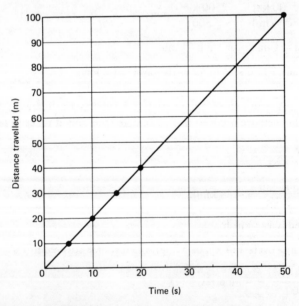

Fig. E1 Distance–time graph

vertical scale by the equivalent value on the horizontal scale. For example, if we take the vertical value of 40 m, it corresponds to a horizontal value of 20 seconds so

$$\text{slope of the line} = \frac{40 \text{ m}}{20 \text{ s}} \quad \text{or} \quad 2 \text{ m/s}$$

If we take the values 100 m and 50 s,

$$\text{slope} = \frac{100 \text{ m}}{50 \text{ s}} = 2 \text{ m/s}$$

Thus the value of the slope of a distance–time graph can be seen to be equal to the speed of the moving object.

We will look at another example.

Example The following data were obtained by studying an electric train travelling at constant speed between two points 1 000 m apart.

Distance from first point (m)	0	100	200	300	400	800	1000
Time travelled (s)	0	4	8	12	16	32	40

Draw a distance–time graph and use it to calculate the speed of the train.

Figure E2 shows the distance–time graph plotted from the figures above. From its slope we should be able to calculate the speed of the train.

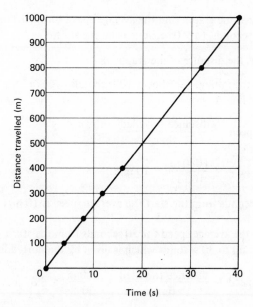

Fig. E2 Distance–time graph

At 40 seconds,

$$\text{slope} = \frac{1000 \text{ m}}{40 \text{ s}} = 25 \text{ m/s}$$

At 25 seconds,

$$\text{slope} = \frac{625 \text{ m}}{25 \text{ s}} = 25 \text{ m/s}$$

The speed of the train is therefore 25 metres per second.

14.4 Calculations of average speeds

If, as is the case in the majority of examples of moving vehicles, the body starts from rest, builds up to a maximum speed, and then slows down to rest, the distance–time graph will not show a straight line but it will still be possible to calculate average speeds.

Example 1 The following table gives the distance moved in metres at different times after a vehicle starts to move from rest, travels for 100 seconds, and stops.

Time from start (s)	0	10	20	30	40	50	60	70	80	90	100
Distance travelled (m)	0	40	100	200	350	500	650	800	900	960	1000

From a distance–time graph, find the average speed for (a) 100 seconds (b) 30 seconds, (c) 70 seconds, (d) 50 seconds from the start.

Figure E3 shows the distance–time graph.

a) To calculate the average speed over 100 seconds, we need the average slope of the dotted line A.

$$\text{Average speed} = \frac{\text{distance travelled}}{\text{time}}$$

$$= \frac{1000 \text{ m}}{100 \text{ s}} = 10 \text{ m/s}$$

i.e. up to 100 seconds from the start the average speed is 10 m/s.

b) To calculate the average speed for 30 seconds from the start, we need the average slope up to 30 seconds which is given by the dotted line B.

$$\text{Average speed} = \frac{\text{distance travelled}}{\text{time}} = \frac{200 \text{ m}}{30 \text{ s}} = 6.67 \text{ m/s}$$

i.e. up to 30 seconds from the start the average speed is 6.67 m/s.

100

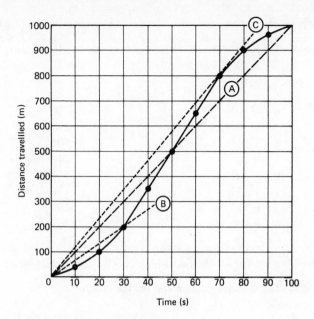

Fig. E3 Distance–time graph for variable-speed motion

c) To calculate the average speed up to 70 seconds we need the average slope of the dotted line C.

$$\text{Average speed} = \frac{\text{distance travelled}}{\text{time}}$$

$$= \frac{800 \text{ m}}{70 \text{ s}} = 11.43 \text{ m/s}$$

i.e. up to 70 seconds from the start the average speed is 11.43 m/s.

d) To calculate the average speed up to 50 seconds we need the average slope up to 50 seconds, which is also given by the dotted line A, as it happens.

$$\text{Average speed} = \frac{\text{distance travelled}}{\text{time}}$$

$$= \frac{500 \text{ m}}{50 \text{ s}} = 10 \text{ m/s}$$

i.e. up to 50 seconds from the start the average speed is 10 m/s.

Example 2 The following figures were obtained for a coach travelling a total distance of 200 km.

101

Time after start of journey (s)	Distance travelled (km)
1 × 10³	10
2 × 10³	20
4 × 10³	40
5 × 10³	46
6 × 10³	50
7 × 10³	70
8 × 10³	104
8.8 × 10³	140
10 × 10³	150
11 × 10³	180
12 × 10³	190
14 × 10³	200

Calculate from a distance—time graph the average speed in m/s and km/h (a) for the complete journey, (b) for the first 1 hour, (c) for the first $2\frac{1}{2}$ hours.

Figure E4 shows the distance—time graph for the coach.

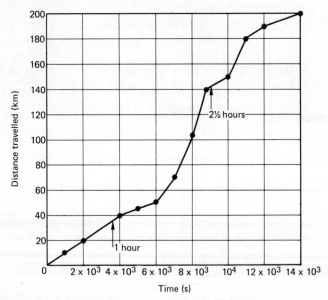

Fig. E4 Distance—time graph for the coach journey in example 2, section 14.4

a) For the complete journey,

$$\text{average speed} = \frac{\text{distance travelled}}{\text{time}}$$

$$= \frac{200 \text{ km}}{14 \times 10^3 \text{ s}}$$

$$= \frac{200 \times 10^3 \text{ m}}{14 \times 10^3 \text{ s}} = 14.29 \text{ m/s}$$

$$= \frac{14.29 \times 3600}{1000} = 51.5 \text{ km/h}$$

i.e. the average speed for the whole journey is 51.5 km/h.

b) For the first hour (1 h = 3.6×10^3 s),

$$\text{average speed} = \frac{\text{distance travelled}}{\text{time}}$$

$$= \frac{36 \times 10^3 \text{ m}}{3.6 \times 10^3 \text{ s}} = 10 \text{ m/s}$$

$$= \frac{10 \times 3600}{1000} = 36 \text{ km/h}$$

i.e. the average speed for the first hour is 36 km/h.

c) For the first $2\frac{1}{2}$ hours ($2.5 \times 3.6 \times 10^3 = 9.0 \times 10^3$ s),

$$\text{average speed} = \frac{\text{distance travelled}}{\text{time}}$$

$$= \frac{142 \times 10^3 \text{ m}}{9.0 \times 10^3 \text{ s}} = 15.8 \text{ m/s}$$

$$= \frac{15.8 \times 3600}{1000} = 56.9 \text{ km/h}$$

i.e. the average speed for the first $2\frac{1}{2}$ hours is 56.9 km/h.

Exercise E1

1. A man walks at 1.75 m/s. (a) What is his speed in km/h? (b) How far will he walk in $2\frac{1}{2}$ hours? (c) How long will it take him to walk 8 km?
2. A car travels at an average speed of 60 km/h. (a) How long does it take to cover 100 m? (b) How far will it travel in 1 second?
3. A lift travels from the bottom to the top of a 100 m building in 12.5 seconds. (a) What is its average speed in m/s? (b) What is its average speed in km/h? (c) How long does it take to travel 80 m?
4. A coach travels at 60 km/h for the first hour of a journey and then at 50 km/h for the next half hour. (a) How far does it travel in $1\frac{1}{2}$ hours? (b) What is its average speed?
5. A cyclist covers 25 km in 80 minutes, then 10 km in 40 minutes, followed by 15 km in 40 minutes. Draw a distance–time graph and from it calculate

103

his average speed (a) for the whole journey, (b) for the first half of the journey.

6. The following figures relate to a train journey between two stations 170 km apart.

Time from start of journey (s)	0	5×10^3	11×10^3	18×10^3	22×10^3	27×10^3	31×10^3	38×10^3	50×10^3
Distance travelled (km)	0 3	16	52	79	115	137	158	170	

Plot a distance—time graph for the journey and determine the average speed for the first (a) 5×10^3 seconds after the start, (b) 20×10^3 seconds after the start, (c) 50×10^3 seconds after the start.

14.5 Speed and velocity

So far, when we have been discussing the speed of the various moving objects in the preceding sections, we have not mentioned the direction in which they have been travelling. Speed is the rate at which distance is covered, regardless of the direction of travel. A quantity that has magnitude and no direction is known as a *scalar* quantity (see section 16.1). Speed is thus a scalar quantity.

If, however, we specify the direction of travel as well as the speed we have *velocity*, and this is a *vector* quantity (see section 16.1). A vector quantity has both magnitude and direction and can be represented by a straight line drawn to scale in the direction of motion. If we consider a train that is travelling at a speed of 100 km/h in a north-easterly direction, we can say that the train has a velocity of 100 km/h north eastwards.

It follows that at any instant the speed and velocity of an object have the same value numerically, the only difference is that with velocity the direction must be specified.

14.6 Acceleration

Acceleration is a term frequently used in connection with motor cycles and cars. We may say that a particular vehicle has good acceleration, which we take to mean that it reaches a particular speed or velocity in a short time.

Acceleration can be defined as *the rate of change of velocity*. If a vehicle starts from a stationary state and reaches 50 km/h in 10 seconds, it will pass through velocities of 10, 20, 30, 40 km/h in this time. So the velocity changes throughout the 10 seconds.

When the brakes are applied on a vehicle moving at 50 km/h, it slows down and eventually stops, passing through all the intermediate velocities until it reaches zero velocity. In scientific terms this is acceleration (as it is a change of velocity), even though it is a negative change.

In section 2.1 we said that one of the possible effects of a force was to change the motion of a body, or accelerate it. When a body is stationary, or when it is moving with a constant velocity, a force acting on the body in any particular direction is exactly balanced by an equal force acting in the opposite direction. In order to make a stationary body move or to change the velocity of a body which is already moving — i.e. to accelerate a body — the force in one direction has to be greater than the force in the opposite direction; in other words, *acceleration results from a net force being applied to a body.*

14.7 Speed–time graphs

Suppose that a car on a flat, horizontal road starts from rest and increases its speed by 2 m/s in the first second, by another 2 m/s in the next second, and so on every second until it reaches a speed of 20 m/s. A table showing the speed of the car at a given time would be as follows:

Time after start (s)	0	1	2	3	4	5	6	7	8	9	10
Speed (m/s)		0	2	4	6	8	10	12	14	16	18	20

If we plot these figures on a graph of speed against time, fig. E5 results. This shows a straight line and in this case we can say that there is uniform acceleration. This means that the speed changes by the same amount every second. The rate of change is 2 metres per second every second, or 2 m/s^2. Accelerations are expressed in units of distance per second per second, m/s^2 being the most common unit.

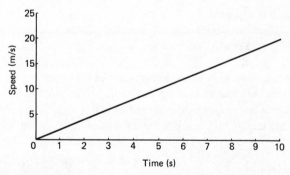

Fig. E5 Speed–time graph

If we consider a more powerful car that increases its speed by 2.5 m/s^2, the speed changes with respect to time as shown below.

Time after start (s)	0	1	2	3	4	5	6	7	8	9	10
Speed (m/s)		0	2.5	5	7.5	10	12.5	15	17.5	20	22.5	25

If we put these figures on a speed–time graph, we obtain fig. E6.

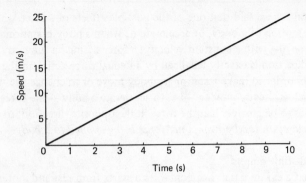

Fig. E6 Speed–time graph

If we compare figs E5 and E6, we can note the following. The car in the second example attains a speed of 20 m/s in a shorter time and in 10 seconds reaches a higher speed, 25 m/s instead of 20 m/s, than the car in the first example. If we were comparing cars, we should say that the second car had the greater acceleration and if we compare the two graphs we can see that the slope of fig. E6 is steeper than that of fig. E5. If we examine these slopes in detail, in fig. E5 the line has a slope of

$$\frac{20 \text{ m/s}}{10 \text{ s}} = 2 \text{ m/s}^2$$

while in fig. E6 the slope is

$$\frac{25 \text{ m/s}}{10 \text{ s}} = 2.5 \text{ m/s}^2$$

The value of the slope gives us the acceleration in every case.

We have said that acceleration can have a negative value when an object is slowing down. If we use the figures given below to plot a speed–time graph for a train that has had its brakes applied at a speed of 45 km/h, fig. E7 results.

Time after applying brakes (s)	0	1	2	3	4	5	6	7	8	9
Speed (km/h)	45	40	35	30	25	20	15	10	5	0

Figure E7 shows a negative slope which has the value 45 km/h ÷ 9 s = 5 km/h s. So the acceleration in this case is −5 km per hour every second or, if we convert it into metres per second per second, the acceleration is equal to −0.14 m/s².

To summarize, if a speed–time graph shows a line which goes *up* from left to right, it indicates that the moving object is increasing in speed, that is the acceleration is positive. If the line goes *down* from left to right it means that the acceleration is negative and the moving object is slowing down. If the line is

106

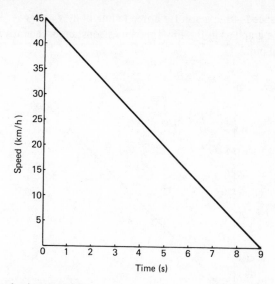

Fig. E7 Speed–time graph

horizontal it means that there is no change in speed and the acceleration is zero. The slope of the line also indicates the magnitude of the acceleration – the steeper the slope, the greater is the value of the acceleration.

14.8 Acceleration of a falling body

Sir Isaac Newton, in his classic studies of gravity, proved that a falling body accelerates on its way to Earth due to the pull of gravity, which is a force due to the attraction of the Earth. He proved that the mass of the body has no effect on this acceleration and that all bodies accelerate at the same rate provided that there is no difference in their resistance to the air. However, in practice, a feather and a coin dropped in air will fall at different rates, due to the larger air resistance of the feather. If they are dropped at the same time in a vacuum, they accelerate at the same rate and reach the bottom of a container at the same time.

A body which falls with no resistance from the air is said to be experiencing free fall and will accelerate constantly under the influence of gravity. (The so-called 'free fall' parachutists accelerate under the pull of gravity but reach a maximum speed when the pull of gravity is balanced by their air resistance.)

The acceleration of a free-falling object, in the scientific sense, is referred to as the acceleration due to gravity and is given the symbol g. The gravitational pull varies slightly over the Earth's surface due to the fact that the Earth is not exactly spherical: $g = 9.832 \text{ m/s}^2$ at the Poles and 9.780 m/s^2 at the Equator; in London, at sea level, it is about 9.81 m/s^2.

If we plot a speed–time graph for a free-falling body where g = 9.81 m/s^2, we shall obtain a graph as in fig. E8. This shows constant acceleration due to the gravitational pull.

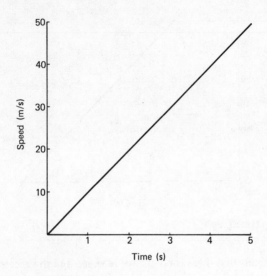

Fig. E8 Speed–time graph for free fall

14.9 Relationship between velocity, time, and distance
We have already said that velocity has the same units as speed but with a specified direction, so, if we use velocity instead of speed, the equation

$$v = \frac{s}{t}$$

where v = average velocity, s = distance travelled, and t = time, is still valid and we can use this equation to solve problems involving these quantities.

14.10 Solution of problems involving acceleration
If we denote by u the initial velocity of an object moving in a straight line, and if the velocity increases uniformly to v after time t, then

> change in velocity = $v - u$

If we call the acceleration a, then

> a = rate of change of velocity

> $\quad = \dfrac{\text{change of velocity}}{\text{time}}$

or $\quad a = \dfrac{v - u}{t}$

or $\quad v = u + at \quad$ (as it is more commonly written)

In order to see the usefulness of this expression, we shall work through some examples.

Example 1 A car has a uniform acceleration of 1 m/s^2 along a straight road. Calculate (a) the velocity after 15 s from standstill, (b) the time taken to reach a velocity of 80 km/h, (c) the time taken for the velocity to increase from 60 to 80 km/h.

a) $\quad v = u + at$

$\qquad = 0 + (1 \text{ m/s}^2 \times 15 \text{ s})$

$\qquad = 15 \text{ m/s}$

$\qquad = \dfrac{15 \times 3600}{1000} = 54 \text{ km/h}$

i.e. after 15 seconds from standstill, the velocity is 54 km/h.

b) $\quad 80 \text{ km/h} = \dfrac{80 \times 1000 \text{ m}}{3600 \text{ s}}$

$\qquad\qquad\qquad = 22.2 \text{ m/s}$

$\qquad\qquad v = u + at$

$\quad 22.2 \text{ m/s} = 0 + (1 \text{ m/s}^2 \times t)$

$\qquad\qquad\quad t = 22.2 \text{ s}$

i.e. it takes 22.2 s to reach 80 km/h.

c) $\quad 60 \text{ km/h} = \dfrac{60 \times 1000 \text{ m}}{3600 \text{ s}}$

$\qquad\qquad\qquad = 16.7 \text{ m/s}$

$\qquad\qquad v = u + at$

$\quad 22.2 \text{ m/s} = 16.7 \text{ m/s} + (1 \text{ m/s}^2 \times t)$

$\qquad\qquad\quad t = (22.2 - 16.7) \text{ s}$

$\qquad\qquad\qquad = 5.5 \text{ s}$

i.e. it will take 5.5 s to accelerate from 60 to 80 km/h.

Example 2   A car is travelling at 15 m/s when its brakes are applied. These slow it down at a rate of 7.5 m/s². Calculate (a) the stopping distance, (b) the speed of the car after 1.5 seconds braking.

a) $v = u + at$

$a = -7.5$ m/s²   (the acceleration is negative)

$v = 0$ (the final velocity is zero)

∴ $0 = 15$ m/s $- (7.5$ m/s² $\times t)$

$t = \dfrac{15 \text{ m/s}}{7.5 \text{ m/s}^2} = 2$ s

It will take the car 2 s to stop. During this time its average velocity is 7.5 m/s (it starts at 15 m/s and stops at zero) so it will travel 15 m; i.e. the stopping distance is 15 m.

b) $v = u + at$

$= 15$ m/s $- (7.5$ m/s² $\times 1.5$ s)

$= (15 - 11.25)$ m/s

$= 3.75$ m/s

i.e. the velocity will be 3.75 m/s after 1.5 seconds braking.

Example 3   A stone is dropped from a balloon. Assuming that the air resistance is negligible, calculate (a) the velocity of the stone after 2 seconds, (b) how long it will take to reach a velocity of 10 m/s, (c) how long it takes for the rate of fall to increase from 60 to 75 m/s².

a) $v = u + at$

$= 0 + (9.81$ m/s² $\times 2$ s)

$= 19.62$ m/s

i.e. the velocity of the stone after 2 seconds is 19.62 m/s.

b) $v = u + at$

10 m/s $= 0 + (9.81$ m/s² $\times t)$

$t = \dfrac{10 \text{ m/s}}{9.81 \text{ m/s}^2} = 1.019$ s

i.e. it will take 1.019 s to reach a velocity of 10 m/s².

c) $v = u + at$

$75 \text{ m/s} = 60 \text{ m/s} + (9.81 \text{ m/s}^2 \times t)$

$$t = \frac{15 \text{ m/s}}{9.81 \text{ m/s}^2} = 1.53 \text{ s}$$

i.e. it will take 1.53 s for the rate of fall to increase from 60 to 75 m/s^2.

Example 4   A ball is thrown vertically upwards with an initial velocity of 25 m/s. Calculate (a) the time taken for it to reach its maximum height, (b) the maximum height it will reach. Neglect air resistance.

a) While the ball is moving upwards it will decelerate due to gravity, so

$a = -9.81 \text{ m/s}^2$

$v = u + at$

$0 = 25 \text{ m/s} - (9.81 \text{ m/s}^2 \times t)$

$$t = \frac{25 \text{ m/s}}{9.81 \text{ m/s}^2} = 2.55 \text{ s}$$

i.e. it will take 2.55 s for the ball to reach its maximum height.

b) Since the ball travels up at an initial speed of 25 m/s and reaches a final speed of zero in 2.55 s,

$$\text{average speed} = \frac{25}{2} \text{ m/s} = 12.5 \text{ m/s}$$

If it travels at this rate for 2.55 s, it will reach a height of

$12.5 \text{ m/s} \times 2.55 \text{ s} = 31.875 \text{ m}$

i.e. the maximum height reached is 31.875 m.

14.11 Angular velocity

When we talk about the speed of a car, we are interested in the distance that it travels in a particular time; but when we talk about the speed of the crankshaft of a car engine we are interested in the rate at which it turns. Speed of rotation is frequently expressed as a number of revolutions per minute, for example record-player turntables rotate at $33\frac{1}{3}$ rev/min or 45 rev/min; however, in several technical applications speed of rotation is often expressed in *radians per second* (rad/s). Since one complete rotation is 2π radians,

$$1 \text{ rev/min} = \frac{\pi}{30} \text{ rad/s}$$

111

As speed of rotation implies direction as well as magnitude, it is a vector quantity and is called *angular velocity* when measured in radians per second.

The angular velocity of a rotating object is *the rate of change of angle turned through about the axis of rotation.*

14.12 Tangential velocity

If a point moves along an arc of a circle of radius r metres, the distance moved along the arc for a rotation of θ radians measured at the centre of the circle is $r\theta$ metres. Thus an angular velocity of θ rad/s corresponds to a tangential velocity of $r\theta$ m/s at a distance r metres from the centre of rotation.

A wheel of radius r metres rotating at n rev/min has a rim velocity of $\dfrac{rn\pi}{30}$ m/s. If the wheel is a pulley wheel, this rim velocity may be imparted to a belt drive in contact with the rim. The straight part of the belt drive is tangential to the curve of the rim of the pulley wheel, hence the speed of the belt can be obtained by calculating the tangential velocity of the pulley wheel at its rim.

Exercise E2

1. If a runner covers 1.5 km in 6 minutes, calculate (a) his average speed in km/h, (b) how long it will take him to run 10 km.
2. A train travels the first 50 km of its journey at an average speed of 80 km/h. What must be its average speed over the next 30 km so that the whole 80 km is covered in 80 minutes?
3. A car travels the first 30 km of a journey at an average speed of 50 km/h. In what time must it cover the next 30 km so that its average speed for the whole journey is 60 km/h?
4. A car covers the first 50 km of its journey in 90 minutes. After stopping for 5 minutes, it travels the remaining 40 km in 1 hour. (a) What is its average speed in kilometres per hour for the whole journey? (b) How long did it take to reach half way?
5. A car starting from rest reaches a speed of 20 m/s in 16 seconds. Assuming uniform acceleration, calculate (a) the acceleration in m/s^2, (b) the distance covered in 10 seconds.
6. The speed of a lorry falls uniformly from 72 km/h to 12 km/h at 3 m/s^2. Calculate (a) the time taken for this fall in speed, (b) how much longer it would take before the lorry stopped.
7. The velocity of a rocket climbing vertically increases with time as shown below:

Time after take-off (s)	0	1	2	3	4	5
Velocity (km/h)	0	20	40	60	80	100

a) Plot a velocity–time graph for the rocket and from it calculate the acceleration in m/s.

b) Assuming uniform acceleration, what will be the velocity of the rocket after 1 minute?

c) How long will it take to attain a velocity of 1200 km/h?

8. A stone projected vertically upwards from a catapult returns to the Earth in 6 seconds. Calculate (a) the velocity with which it leaves the catapult, (b) the height that it reaches.

9. The following table refers to the velocity at 1 second intervals of a ball thrown vertically upwards:

Time (s)	0	1	2	3	4	5	6
Velocity (m/s)	29.43	19.62	9.81	0	9.81	19.62	29.43

Draw a velocity–time graph for the ball and calculate (a) the maximum height reached by the ball, (b) the two times at which the ball is travelling at exactly half its maximum velocity.

10. The velocity of a moving vehicle increases uniformly from 10 km/h to 100 km/h while it travels 200 m. Calculate (a) the acceleration in m/s^2, (b) the time taken in seconds.

15 Friction

If we try to pull a sledge across a frozen pond, it will move comparatively easily; however, if the same sledge is pulled along a dry road it requires a much greater force to move it. The difficulty experienced in moving an object over a given surface is due to 'friction'. In this section we shall see that friction is a measurable force and we will look at the factors that affect the size of this force.

15.1 Friction as a force

Friction can be defined as *a force opposing the sliding of one surface over another*. It acts at the surface of contact between two bodies in a direction opposite to that of the motion.

If we consider a solid block of stone resting on a horizontal bench (fig. E9), it is acted upon by a downward force W due to the pull of gravity. There is also acting upon it an upward reaction R at right angles ('normal') to the surface of contact. This upward normal reaction is equal and opposite to force W, so no motion occurs.

If a horizontal force Q is applied to the block, pulling towards the left as in fig. E10, the block does not move until Q reaches a certain value. This is due to the existence of a force F in the opposite direction exerted on the block by the table. When Q is larger than F, movement to the left occurs. When the block of stone is at rest – that is, when Q exactly balances F – the solid is said to be in

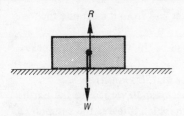

Fig. E9 Forces acting on a solid
body resting on a horizontal bench

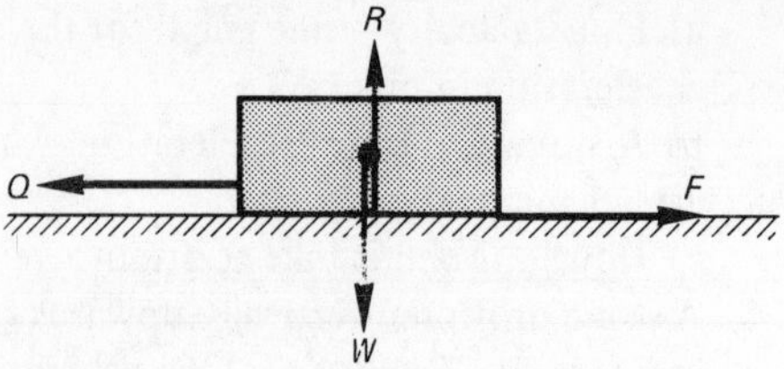

Fig. E10 Forces acting on a solid body
pulled across a horizontal bench

equilibrium. The force F which resists the movement due to a horizontal force Q is called the *friction force* and it is measured in newtons, the units used to measure all forces.

15.2 Factors affecting friction-force size and direction

The size of the friction force F varies with the size of the pull exerted on the body by the force Q. It will exactly balance Q so that there will be no movement of the body until Q reaches a certain value. Below this critical value the force of friction will automatically adjust to balance the force exerting a pull on the body.

When the body starts to move, $Q = F$, so the force Q is overcoming the drag due to friction and the pull downwards due to the weight of the body. The maximum value of the friction force F which occurs when the body is just about to move is called the *limiting friction force*. A term called the *coefficient of friction*, denoted by the Greek letter μ (*'mu'*) is defined as *the limiting friction force (F) divided by the normal reaction (R)*:

$$\mu = \frac{F}{R}$$

or $F = \mu R$

The coefficient of friction is a property of the particular two surfaces in contact, and the higher its value the greater the force required to pull one surface over the other. As it is a ratio of forces, it has no units.

Example 1   A block of metal has a mass of 100 kg and requires a horizontal force of 250 N to drag it at constant speed along a horizontal floor. Calculate the coefficient of friction.

Weight of metal $= 100 \text{ kg} \times 9.81 \text{ m/s}^2 = 981 \text{ N}$

∴ Normal reaction $R = 981 \text{ N}$

Friction force $F = 250 \text{ N}$

114

$$\mu = \frac{F}{R}$$

$$= \frac{250 \text{ N}}{981 \text{ N}} = 0.255$$

i.e. the coefficient of friction is 0.255.

Example 2 The coefficient of friction for a stone block sliding on a horizontal floor is 0.35. Calculate the horizontal force required to slide a 100 kg block of stone along the floor.

Weight of stone $= 100 \text{ kg} \times 9.81 \text{ m/s}^2 = 981 \text{ N}$

$\therefore$ Normal reaction $R = 981 \text{ N}$

$F = \mu R$

$= 0.35 \times 9.81 \text{ N}$

$= 339.3 \text{ N}$

i.e. the force required is 339.3 N.

Example 3 If the stone in example 2 weighed 200 kg, what force would be required to move it?

Normal reaction $R = 200 \text{ kg} \times 9.81 \text{ m/s}^2$

$= 1962 \text{ N}$

$F = \mu R$

$= 0.35 \times 1962 \text{ N}$

$= 678.6 \text{ N}$

i.e. a force of 678.6 N would be required.

Example 4 If water on the floor in example 2 lowered the value of μ to 0.25, what force would be required to move the 100 kg block?

$R = 981 \text{ N}$

$F = \mu R$

$= 0.25 \times 981 \text{ N}$

$= 245.2 \text{ N}$

i.e. a force of 245.2 N would be required.

The above examples show the factors that can affect the force necessary to overcome friction and cause a body to slide over another surface.

To summarize, we can say:

i) as the weight of the body increases, so the normal reaction and the friction force increase;

ii) as the coefficient of friction increases, so the friction force increases.

It can also be shown by experiment that for dry solid surfaces the friction force is not affected by the areas of the surfaces in contact or by the speed of sliding.

15.3 Examples of friction in practice

One of the commonest uses of the force of friction is in the brake systems of all kinds of vehicles. The force of friction can be used to slow down and bring to a stop rotating shafts, discs, or drums — substances with high coefficients of friction are used for this purpose. Due to friction, mechanical energy is converted to thermal energy, so the materials used for brake systems also have to possess heat-resistant properties.

Other applications where friction is a desirable property are clutch systems, tyres on a road, and belts connecting pulleys.

However, in the majority of engineering applications friction is undesirable, as friction between moving parts results in energy that would be used in useful work being used to overcome the friction and being lost as heat. For this reason, lubrication is used to produce a film of oil or grease over the moving parts and prevent them from coming into direct contact with each other.

The type of lubrication system used depends on many factors, the most important being the pressure between the moving parts, the temperature of operation, the speed of operation, and the nature of the movement (rotating or reciprocating). In systems where high pressures are encountered, greases are used instead of oils, as oils would be squeezed out of the spaces between the moving parts. For high-temperature operation, lubricants which do not decompose under the influence of temperature are used — graphite, molybdenum disulphide, or silicone-based lubricants are frequently employed. For high-speed systems, where the oil would be thrown out of the system, forced lubrication in which oil is pumped to the point where it is needed is frequently used.

One of the best lubricants is air, and the hovercraft principle, which uses a layer of air between the bottom of the craft and the ground, reduces the friction force considerably, so a hovercraft requires much less force for its lateral movement than if it were running on the ground.

The science of tribology, which studies the phenomena occurring between moving surfaces, is a complex one, and simple experiments do not give much guidance as to what is happening at the interface between moving bodies.

Exercise E3

1. A machine of mass 1 tonne requires a force of 1300 N to slide it at a uniform speed across a horizontal floor. Calculate (a) the coefficient of friction, (b) what force would be needed to remove the machine if the coefficient of friction was reduced by 30% by polishing the floor.

2. A mass of 10 tonnes is slid over a rough horizontal surface where the co-efficient of friction is 0.45. Calculate (a) the force required, (b) the work done if the mass is moved 100 m, (c) the power required to carry out this work in 30 minutes.

3. A glass dish rests on a horizontal wooden surface. When it contains 5 kg of sand, it is found that a horizontal force of 15 N causes it to move. If 3 kg of sand are removed from the dish it is found that the force required to move it is exactly halved. Calculate (a) the mass of the dish, (b) the coefficient of friction.

4. A 10 tonne mass rests on a horizontal surface. Calculate (a) the force required to move this mass if the coefficient of friction is 0.35, (b) what mass can be moved by the same force if sand is spread on the surface and increases the coefficient of friction to 0.45.

F   Statics

16 Forces in static equilibrium

We have looked at bodies in motion and have examined the effects of forces on moving bodies. Forces can act on stationary bodies without producing movement and on moving bodies without producing any change in either the speed or the direction of movement. This is due to the fact that for every force there is an equal and opposite force of resistance or *reaction* which maintains equilibrium. The branch of science known as statics studies the relationship between forces and their reactions in both solids and fluids.

16.1 Scalar and vector quantities

We have already used the terms '*scalar*' and '*vector*' quantities in section 14.5. We have defined a *vector* quantity as *a quantity that has magnitude and direction. A quantity that has only magnitude* is a *scalar* quantity.

Quantities such as mass, time, and speed possess only magnitude and are examples of scalar quantities.

Quantities such as force and velocity, however, have both magnitude and direction and are vector quantities. A force possesses magnitude, direction, and a point of application. In order to define a force exactly, its *sense* must also be given. Figure F1 represents a mass M suspended from a ring by a cord. This mass will have acting on it downwards a force W = mass × acceleration due to gravity (Mg) which is its weight. As it remains stationary and does not fall downwards, an opposite and equal force (or reaction) P must act upwards. Both W and P are forces acting vertically, but the *sense* of W is downwards and the *sense* of P is upwards.

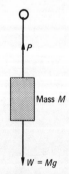

Fig. F1 Forces on a
suspended mass

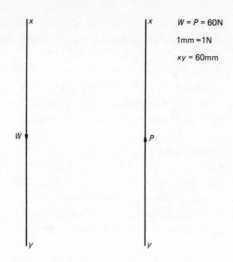

$W = P = 60N$

$1mm = 1N$

$xy = 60mm$

Fig. F2 Forces represented by vectors

We can represent these forces by vectors (fig. F2). In this, if the weight of M is 60 N, then W is a force of 60 N acting vertically downwards from x to y, and the reaction P is a force of 60 N acting vertically upwards from y to x. The direction of the force is indicated by the arrowhead and the scale of the vectors is such that 1 mm is equivalent to 1 newton.

16.2 Stable, unstable, and neutral equilibrium

A body is said to be in equilibrium when every force acting on it is exactly balanced by an equal force acting in the opposite direction, so there is no net force acting on the body.

Imagine a ball bearing resting inside a concave surface as shown in fig. F3(a). It is in equilibrium. If the ball bearing is moved slightly to one side, it will roll back into its original position of equilibrium. Such a system, in which an object displaced slightly from its equilibrium position will return to the equilibrium position, is said to be in *stable equilibrium*.

Now imagine the ball bearing balanced on top of a convex surface as shown in fig. F3(b); if it is moved slightly to one side it will continue to move farther

(a) Stable   (b) Unstable   (c) Neutral

Fig. F3 Types of equilibrium

away from its equilibrium position. A system in which an object displaced slightly from its equilibrium position will continue to move away from the equilibrium position is said to be in *unstable equilibrium*.

If, however, the ball bearing is placed on a smooth level surface as in fig. F3(c), it can rest in equilibrium at any position on the surface and if it is moved slightly from one equilibrium position it will rest in equilibrium in its new position. Such a system is said to be in *neutral equilibrium*.

16.3 The moment of force about a point
Figure F4 shows a uniform thin strip of steel which has a hole drilled at its mid-point Y. If this strip has a rod pushed through the hole so that it can turn freely, then, provided that the hole is exactly at the centre and the strip of steel is completely uniform, there is no tendency for the strip to rotate in either direction about Y as long as no external force is applied to it.

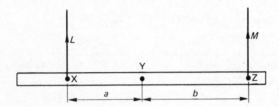

Fig. F4 Moments of a force

If the hook of a spring balance is attached to the rod through a hole at X, an upward force L applied by this balance will cause the rod to rotate in a clockwise direction about the pivoting rod at Y. If the spring balance at X is removed and a force M is applied by another balance through a hole at Z, the strip will turn anticlockwise.

The tendency of a force to produce rotation of a body about a point is called *the moment of the force about the point* and is *equal to the force multiplied by the distance from the point* (see fig. F5). If the force is expressed in newtons and the length in metres, the unit of the moment is the newton metre.

16.4 Principle of moments
If we use the strip in fig. F4 and apply two forces L and M to it at the same time, through spring balances, so that the strip is kept horizontal, we should find that the balance which is nearer to the centre would show a larger reading (L) than the balance further away (M).

If we measure the distance from X to Y and call it a and from Y to Z and call it b, we should find that, whatever the actual values in millimetres and newtons, the moment of the forces L and M exerted by the spring balances,

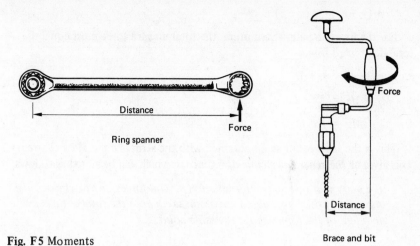

Fig. F5 Moments

Brace and bit

that is $L \times a$ and $M \times b$, are always equal. $L \times a$ is called the clockwise moment of L about Y and $M \times b$ is called the anticlockwise moment of M about Y, so, for equilibrium,

$La = Mb$

This relationship is known as the *principle of moments.*

We have already considered the special case of a strip pivoted at its centre. If we consider a strip pivoted at a point K and not at its centre C (fig. F6), it will again be found that

the anticlockwise moment of L about point K $= L(x - z)$

the clockwise moment of M about point K $= M(y + z)$

and   the anticlockwise moment of R about point K $= Rz$

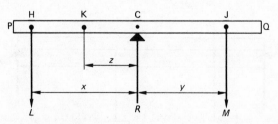

Fig. F6 Principle of moments

If the strip remains horizontal under the influence of these moments, then the clockwise moments must be equal to the anticlockwise moments, or

$$M(y + z) = L(x - z) + Rz$$

For the beam to be in equilibrium, the total upward force must equal the total downward force,

$$\therefore \qquad R = L + M$$

$$\therefore \quad My + Mz = Lx - Lz + Lz + Mz$$

$$My = Lx$$

This is the same result as we obtained with the strip pivoted at its centre. This gives us *the general principle of moments*, which can be stated as follows:

> *if a body is at rest under the action of several forces, the total clockwise moment of the forces about any point is equal to the total anticlockwise moment of the forces about the same point.*

16.5 Beam problems
In order to make sure that the principle of moments and its implications are fully understood, we shall have a look at some simple problems involving the principle. One of the simplest cases is a beam supported at its two ends and loaded at a point somewhere along its length. Figure F7 shows a beam PQ of length 5 m supported at its ends P and Q with a 10 kg mass hanging from a point S which is 2 m from Q. The force acting downwards at S will be equal to the weight of the 10 kg mass, that is

$$10 \text{ kg} \times 9.81 \text{ m/s}^2 = 98.1 \text{ N}$$

If we neglect the weight of the beam, the suspended mass will exert downward forces on the supports at P and Q, and these supports will exert exactly equal and opposite (upward) reactions on the beam. If we call the reactions R_P and R_Q, they must together equal the weight suspended at S, otherwise the beam would move. So we can say

$$R_P + R_Q = 98.1 \text{ N}$$

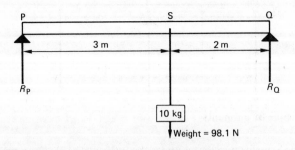

Fig. F7 A beam supported at its ends and loaded

122

We can work out the values of R_P and R_Q by taking moments about a point on the beam. If we take point Q first, the problem is simplified as the reaction R_Q will have a zero moment about Q, since its distance from Q is zero.

If we now consider the force due to the weight at S tending to turn the beam anticlockwise about point Q, this is exactly balanced by the reaction R_P acting upwards at P, so, if we take moments about Q, the principle of moments states

force at P x distance of this force from Q = force at S x distance of this force from Q

$$R_P \times 5 \text{ m} = 98.1 \text{ N} \times 2\text{m}$$

$$R_P = \frac{98.1 \text{ N} \times 2 \text{ m}}{5 \text{ m}}$$

$$R_P = 39.24 \text{ N}$$

If we had considered the moments about point P, the principle of moments would have given us

force at Q x distance of this force from P = force at S x distance of this force from Q

$$R_Q \times 5 \text{ m} = 98.1 \text{ N} \times 3 \text{ m}$$

$$R_Q = \frac{98.1 \text{ N} \times 3 \text{ m}}{5 \text{ m}}$$

$$= 58.86 \text{ N}$$

We can check that this is in fact correct as we have said that

$$R_P + R_Q = 98.1 \text{ N}$$

and we can see that 39.24 N added to 58.86 N does give 98.1 N. So, if we had calculated R_P first, it would have been simple to determine R_Q by subtracting R_P from the total downward force.

We neglected the weight of the beam in the example above, but in practice this must affect the downward load on the supports at the end. If the mass of the beam in the example is 2 kg, its weight is 19.62 N. As the beam is uniform, this load is distributed equally between the two supports, so the reactions at P and Q must both be increased by half the downward force due to the weight of the beam, 9.81 N in each case. This means that the total reactions at P and Q are

$$R_P = 39.24 + 9.81 = 49.05 \text{ N}$$

and $R_Q = 58.86 + 9.81 = 68.67 \text{ N}$

16.6 Centre of gravity

In the problems we have solved concerning horizontal beams, the weight of the beam has been considered to be equally carried by the two supports. This is a true picture as long as the two supports are equally spaced from the centre of the beam. However, if the supports are not equidistant from the centre, the two reactions due to the weight of the beam will not be equal. For simple problems involving horizontal beams we can consider the weight of the beam as acting through a point in the beam called its *centre of gravity* (c.g.).

The centre of gravity of a body is the point in that body at which its mass may be regarded as being concentrated and through which its weight acts vertically.

The location of the centre of gravity does not depend on the position of the body. This implies that, if the body rests suspended by a cord from the centre of gravity, the vertical upward force exerted by the cord is equal to the weight of the body and its line of action passes through the centre of gravity.

The centre of gravity is the point through which the resultant force equal to the weight of the body passes.

Example A uniform beam AB of length 3 m (fig. F8) is supported at each end and a mass of 5 kg is suspended at a point C on the beam. The mass of the beam is 0.2 kg and the reactions at A and B are 17.33 N and 33.68 N. Calculate the distance of the point C from A.

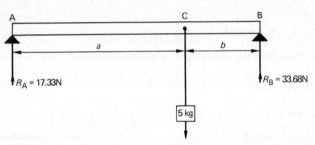

Fig. F8 A loaded horizontal beam

The load due to the mass of 5 kg = 5 kg × 9.81 m/s^2 = 49.05 N

The mass of the beam is 0.2 kg, so the load due to this is 0.2 kg × 9.81 m/s^2 = 1.96 N. As the beam is uniform, this force can be regarded as acting downward through the centre of gravity, i.e. at the mid-point of the beam.

Then, taking moments about A,

clockwise moment = anticlockwise moment

$(49.05 \text{ N} \times \text{AC}) + (1.96 \text{ N} \times \frac{1}{2}\text{AB}) = 33.68 \text{ N} \times \text{AB}$

124

$$\therefore \quad AC = \frac{(33.68 \text{ N} \times 3 \text{ m}) - (1.96 \text{ N} \times 1.5 \text{ m})}{49.05 \text{ N}}$$

$$= \frac{(101.04 - 2.94) \text{ N m}}{49.05 \text{ N}}$$

$$= 2 \text{ m}$$

i.e. point C is 2 m from A.

16.7 Position of centre of gravity

The centres of gravity of some simple solids are shown in fig. F9:

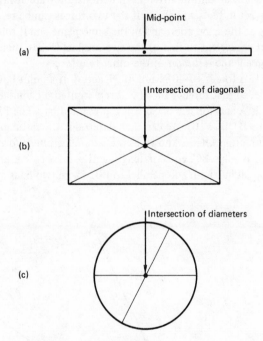

Fig. F9 Centres of gravity of uniform solids

a) for a rod, the centre of gravity is at the centre point of the rod;
b) for a rectangular lamina — that is a plate of uniform thickness — the centre of gravity will be found where the diagonals cross;
c) for a circular lamina, the centre of gravity is where two diameters intersect, that is the centre of the circle.

It is relatively easy to check whether a point is the centre of gravity of a solid body — it is the one point from which the body can be suspended so that it remains in whatever position it is placed. If we were to suspend the rod in fig. F9(a) by a point a short distance from the centre, it would tilt from the horizontal. If the rectangular lamina in fig. F9(b) were suspended from a point above the intersections of the diagonals, it would not remain in any position other than with its long sides at right angles to the cord. However, if each of these solids was suspended from its centre of gravity, it would remain in position at any angle to the cord in which it was placed.

When any solid body is suspended from a single point, it will rotate until its centre of gravity is vertically below the point of suspension.

16.8 Resultant of two coplanar forces

When two forces act at a point in different directions, they are always coplanar, that is to say they act in the same plane. If the two forces can be replaced by a single force acting at the same point and in the same plane and if this single force has an effect equivalent to that of the two original forces, then we say that this single force is the *resultant* of the other two forces.

If we examine two forces, of 40 N and 80 N, acting at a point P, we can draw them to scale, so that force *A* of 40 N is represented by a line PA 40 mm long acting towards A and force *B* of 80 N is represented by a line PB 80 mm long acting towards B (fig. F10). We can then determine the resultant of these two forces by completing what is known as the *parallelogram of forces*. To do this, we draw from B a line BQ, equal in length and parallel to PA, and from A another line AQ equal in length and parallel to PB. These two lines meet at Q.

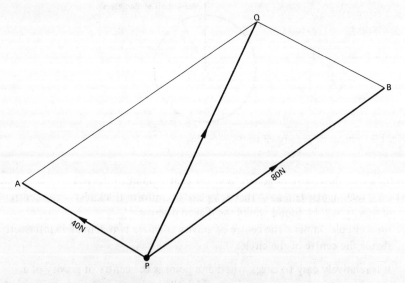

Fig. F10 Resultant of two forces acting at a point P

126

If we join P and Q we have a line 70 mm long. On our scale this represents a force of 70 N, and in fact the resultant of the two forces we have drawn is 70 N in the direction PQ.

Exercise F1

1. With the aid of sketches, show what is meant by (a) stable, (b) unstable, (c) neutral equilibrium.
2. Figure F11 shows a uniform beam which is pivoted at its mid-point C. A body of mass 2 kg is suspended at point D. Calculate the mass m that has to be suspended at point B to maintain the beam in balance.

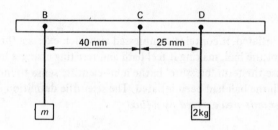

Fig. F11 Exercise F1, problem 2

3. A beam AB 3.5 m long rests on a pivot C, 1.5 m from A. There is a downward force of 100 N acting at A. Calculate (a) the force required at B to maintain equilibrium and (b) the force acting at the pivot. Neglect the weight of the beam.
4. A beam AB 2 m long is pivoted at end A. A mass of 5 kg is suspended at a point X, 1.2 m from A. Calculate the vertical force at B that would keep the beam horizontal. Neglect the weight of the beam.
5. A horizontal beam of uniform section 10 m long rests on two supports, one 1 m from one end of the beam, the other 4 m from the other end of the beam. The mass of the beam is 200 kg. Calculate the upward reactions of the supports.
6. If a mass of 1 tonne is applied to the centre of the beam in question 5, what will the upward reactions of the supports be?
7. Two men carry a scaffolding pole 12 m long of mass 100 kg. One man is 2 m from the end and the other is 3 m from the other end. Find the force exerted by the pole on each man's supporting shoulder.
8. Forces of 3 N and 5 N act at the same point. If the angle between the lines of action of the two forces is 60°, construct a parallelogram of forces to a scale of 10 mm ≡ 1 N and measure the diagonal to determine the magnitude of the resultant.

127

9. If equal forces at a point act in directions north, east, and south, what is the direction of their resultant?

10. Find the angle between two forces, of 8 N and 15 N, which act at the same point if their resultant is 17 N.

17 Pressure in fluids

When we wish to talk about a substance that is not a solid, we can call it a fluid, which means that it is able to flow. Liquids and gases are both *fluids*.

In this section we shall look at what is understood by the term 'pressure', how pressure acts in a fluid, and how this pressure can be calculated or measured.

17.1 Pressure

When a football is inflated, it contains compressed air which exerts a thrust outwards on the case of the ball, making it feel hard and resisting changes in its shape. We would use the term 'pressure' in the non-scientific sense to indicate the degree to which the ball had been inflated. The scientific definition of *pressure* is *the force per unit area exerted by a fluid*.

17.2 The units of pressure

The force acting on the surface is measured in newtons, so pressure will be measured in newtons per square metre (N/m^2). This unit (N/m^2) is sometimes known as the *pascal* (Pa) to acknowledge the work of the French scientist and philosopher Blaise Pascal (1623–62) in the science of fluids. Larger pressures are frequently expressed in kilonewtons per square metre (kN/m^2) or meganewtons per square metre (MN/m^2).

One other unit which may be encountered in the measurement of pressure is the *bar*. 1 bar $= 10^5 \ N/m^2$ and is approximately equal to the pressure of the atmosphere at sea level. The *millibar*, which equals 10^{-3} bar or $10^2 \ N/m^2$, is the unit generally used by meteorologists for the measurement of pressure.

17.3 Calculation of pressure

As we have seen in the preceding section, pressure is a measure of force per unit area, so, if a force of 5 kN acts on a surface whose area is $100 \ m^2$, the pressure on this surface is given by

$$\text{pressure} = \frac{\text{force (N)}}{\text{area (m}^2)} = \frac{5 \times 10^3 \ N}{100 \ m^2} = 50 \ N/m^2$$

Similarly, if a force of 65 N acts on an area of $1 \ mm^2$,

$$\text{pressure} = \frac{\text{force (N)}}{\text{area (m}^2)} = \frac{65 \ N}{10^{-6} \ m^2} = 65 \ MN/m^2$$

Also, if a force of 1 kN acts on an area of 1 mm^2,

$$\text{pressure} = \frac{\text{force (N)}}{\text{area (m}^2)} = \frac{1000 \text{ N}}{10^{-6} \text{ m}^2} = 1000 \text{ MN/m}^2$$

17.4 The factors that determine the pressure at any point in a fluid

In order to examine the forces acting in a fluid, let us consider a tank of uniform cross-sectional area a, containing a liquid whose density is ρ. If the tank has a depth h, then the pressure on the base of the tank due to the liquid in it is equal to the force acting on the base divided by the area of the base.

$$\text{Pressure on base} = \frac{\text{force due to liquid}}{\text{area of base}} = \frac{\text{weight of liquid}}{\text{area of base}}$$

$$= \frac{\text{mass of liquid} \times \text{acceleration due to gravity}}{\text{area of base}}$$

$$= \frac{\text{density of liquid} \times \text{volume of liquid} \times g}{\text{area of base}}$$

$$= \frac{\rho \times ah \times g}{a}$$

$$= \rho g h$$

If ρ is in kg/m^3, g is in m/s^2, and h is in m, then p will be in N/m^2.

There is, however, one other factor that has to be considered in determining the pressure acting in a liquid. That is the effect of the pressure of the atmosphere outside the container. This acts on the surface of the liquid and has to be added to the pressure due to the liquid. So the pressure (p) at any depth in a liquid is given by

$$p = \rho g h + A$$

where A is the atmospheric pressure.

Example 1 An open tank contains oil of density 800 kg/m^3. Calculate the pressure exerted at depths of 1 m and 2 m if the atmospheric pressure is 100 kN/m^2.

$$p = \rho g h + A$$

$$\text{At 1 m,} \quad p = (800 \text{ kg/m}^3 \times 9.81 \text{ m/s}^2 \times 1 \text{ m}) + 100 \times 10^3 \text{ N/m}^2$$

$$= 7850 \text{ N/m}^2 + 100\,000 \text{ N/m}^2 = 107\,850 \text{ N/m}^2$$

$$= 107.85 \text{ kN/m}^2$$

i.e. the pressure at a depth of 1 m is 107.85 kN/m^2.

At 2 m, p = $(800 \text{ kg/m}^3 \times 9.81 \text{ m/s}^2 \times 2 \text{ m}) + 100 \times 10^3 \text{ N/m}^2$

$$= 15\,700 \text{ N/m}^2 + 100\,000 \text{ N/m}^2 = 115\,700 \text{ N/m}^2$$

$$= 115.7 \text{ kN/m}^2$$

i.e. the pressure at a depth of 2 m is 115.7 kN/m^2.

Example 2   An open cylindrical tank contains water. If the atmospheric pressure above the tank is 98.1 kN/m^2, calculate the depth at which the pressure is twice that of the atmosphere.

$$p = \rho g h + A$$

$$2 \times 9.81 \times 10^3 \text{ N/m}^2 = (1000 \text{ kg/m}^3 \times 9.81 \text{ m/s}^2 \times h \text{ m}) + 9.81 \times 10^3 \text{ N/m}^2$$

$$9.81 \times 10^3 \text{ N/m}^2 = 9810h \text{ N/m}^2$$

$$h = \frac{98\,100}{9810} = 10$$

i.e. the pressure is twice that of the atmosphere at a depth of 10 m.

17.5 Properties of pressure in a liquid
We can see from the two examples above, and the formula for pressure at any depth in a given liquid, that the area of the liquid or the container that it is in does not affect the pressure. This gives us an important property of pressure in a liquid:

the pressure in a liquid is independent of the shape of the containing vessel.

Another property of pressure that is important is that

at any given level in a liquid, the pressure is equal in all directions.

This can be seen to be true by watching a bubble rise through a liquid. As soon as it becomes visible it is spherical, and as it rises to the top of the liquid it remains spherical. If the pressure acted more in one direction than in another, the bubble would be flattened at some part of its surface.

The third property of pressure in a fluid is that

pressure acts in a direction normal to its containing surface.

17.6 Measurement of gas pressure
We have seen in section 17.4 that the pressure at any point in a fluid depends on the density of the fluid, the depth of the point below the surface of the fluid, and the local acceleration due to gravity. At any particular place, the acceleration due to gravity is constant, so the pressure in a fluid will vary only with density and depth. If the density of the fluid is constant then the pressure

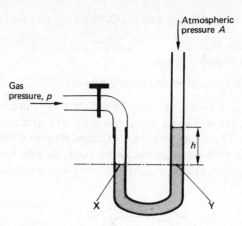

Fig. F12 Manometer

will vary only with depth, and this forms the basis of the instrument known as the *manometer*, which may be used to measure the pressure in a gas supply.

A simple U-tube manometer is shown in fig. F12 – it consists of a U-shaped tube partly filled with liquid – usually water or mercury. If both ends of the tube are open to the atmosphere so that the same pressure acts on the liquid surface in each arm, the liquid levels in the two arms will be found to be equal and at the same depth below the surface in each arm the pressure will be the atmospheric pressure plus a pressure due to the weight of the liquid varying only with depth – thus the pressure in the two arms at any level will be the same.

To find the pressure of a gas supply, one end of the U-tube is connected by a flexible tube to a tapping in the gas supply and the other end is left open to the atmosphere. When the gas supply is turned on, the liquid level will rise in the arm open to the atmosphere until equilibrium is reached, as shown in the figure.

The pressure at any level in the liquid is the same in the two arms. At equilibrium the pressure p at X (the pressure of the gas supply) will be equal to the pressure at Y, which is the atmospheric pressure A plus the pressure due to the height h of liquid in the open arm,

i.e. $p = A + \rho g h$

Thus, if the atmospheric pressure at the time is known, the pressure of the gas supply can be found from a knowledge of the density of the liquid and the local acceleration due to gravity.

The pressure found using this equation is known as the *absolute pressure* – it is the actual force per unit area concerned. Sometimes, however, a quantity called *gauge pressure* is used – this gives only the amount by which the force

131

per unit area due to the gas supply exceeds the force per unit area due to atmospheric pressure;

i.e.   gauge pressure $= \rho g h$

absolute pressure $= \rho g h +$ atmospheric pressure

Another method of measuring pressure in a gas is to use a pressure gauge such as the Bourdon pressure gauge. As shown in fig. F13, this consists of a flattened metal tube T bent into an arc and attached through a lever to a ratchet and gear wheel G. As the pressure of the gas increases, the tube tends to straighten and the closed end moves, causing a pointer to move over a calibrated scale.

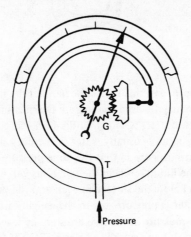

Fig. F13 Bourdon gauge

Exercise F2

1. Calculate the pressure exerted on the floor by the heel of a woman's shoe supporting a weight of 500 N if the area of the heel is (a) 80 mm², (b) 3200 mm².

2. If the atmospheric pressure above a lake is 100 kN/m², calculate the depth at which the pressure is three times that of the atmosphere.

3. An open tank contains a liquid whose density is 900 kg/m³. Calculate the depth in the tank at which the pressure is 100 kN/m² if atmospheric pressure is 98 kN/m³.

4. A plastic water tank has a maximum safe working pressure of 120 kN/m². If the atmospheric pressure is 100 kN/m², calculate the maximum depth of water the tank can safely hold.

G   Chemical reactions

In this section we shall look at chemical reactions — these occur when two or more substances are brought into contact with each other and one or more of the substances undergoes some form of change in its nature. Corrosion or rusting is an example of a chemical reaction. Other reactions may be brought about by passing an electric current, and we shall also consider these.

18 Oxidation

18.1 Composition of air
The air that we breathe is a mixture, in that its composition is not fixed and varies slightly from place to place depending on whether one is inland or on the coast, near to industry or out in the country, in a wet or a dry climate, near sea level or at a great height, to name just a few of the variables that can affect the composition of air. The gas that is extracted from air by our lungs when we breathe is oxygen, but this constitutes approximately only one fifth of air. By far the biggest proportion of air is made up of the gas nitrogen which is a colourless, odourless gas, heavier than oxygen, and which, on its own, would cause suffocation. There are several other minor constituents present in air, and Table G1 gives the approximate composition of air.

Gas	% by volume
Nitrogen	78
Oxygen	21
Carbon dioxide	0.03
Other gases	0.97

Table G1 Approximate composition of air

18.2 Oxidation of copper
If we were to weigh exactly 100 grams of pure copper turnings and put them in a fireclay dish inside a heat-resistant glass tube and then pass air slowly over the copper while it was heated to about 750 °C, we should find after some time that the bright copper turnings would have become darker in colour and would disintegrate. If we weighed them again we should find that the weight would have increased by approximately 25 grams. This would have occurred since the

133

copper had absorbed oxygen from the air and changed into copper oxide (CuO). For approximately every 64 grams of copper, 16 grams of oxygen are needed to produce copper oxide.

If it were possible to collect some of the air that had been passed over the copper, chemical analysis would show us that the proportion of oxygen in it had decreased.

What has in fact happened is that the copper has been *oxidized* and a chemical reaction that can be represented by the following equation has occurred:

$$2\,Cu + O_2 = 2\,CuO$$

which in words means

> two atoms of copper + one atom of oxygen change to two molecules of copper oxide.

18.3 Combination with oxygen

In the previous section we have seen how copper combines with the oxygen in the air when it is heated. This is what happens when something burns in air. If we set fire to a piece of paper and drop it into a jar which we then seal, the paper will burn for a short time and then go out. What is happening is that the paper, which is composed of carbon atoms combined with various other elements, is combining with the oxygen in the air and changing its chemical composition. This carries on until all the oxygen in the jar is used up, then it stops. This process, which is known as *combustion*, is an example of a chemical reaction which produces heat. Once the reaction has been given a start by a flame, the heat source can be taken away and the reaction will give off sufficient heat to keep itself going for as long as oxygen is available. This is typical of many reactions between oxygen and other substances. All *combustion*, or burning in air, is really *a chemical reaction between the burning substance and the oxygen in the air with the evolution of sufficient heat to keep the reaction going*.

18.4 Oxides

If an element reacts with oxygen (e.g. the copper in section 18.2) it produces a compound of itself and the oxygen. The *compounds* of this type *which contain only atoms of the original element and atoms of oxygen* are called *oxides*. Each oxide has a fixed composition, but some substances can form more than one sort of oxide depending on various factors, which may include the amount of oxygen available for the reaction and the temperature at which the reaction takes place. Iron, for example, can form three oxides: FeO, which is known as wüstite, and two more common oxides, Fe_2O_3 (haematite) and Fe_3O_4 (magnetite). In each of these oxides, the amount of oxygen in combination with the iron is different.

134

Although the oxides of the majority of elements are solid at room temperature, there are one or two notable exceptions. The two oxides formed when carbon burns in air — CO (carbon monoxide) and CO_2 (carbon dioxide) — are both gases at normal temperatures, but they have very different properties. The oxide of hydrogen (H_2O) is a very well-known liquid, but can be converted to a solid below $0\,^\circ C$ and to a gas above $100\,^\circ C$.

18.5 Rusting

A chemical reaction that involves the formation of an oxide of iron costs thousands of millions of pounds every year and practically every motor vehicle shows an example of it. It is, of course, the oxidation of iron known as 'rusting'. The characteristic red colour of rusty iron and steel is due to the formation on its surface of the oxide of iron known as haematite (Fe_2O_3). This oxide, when it occurs as rust however, has chemically combined with it a certain proportion of water to give what is known as a *hydrated* oxide of iron.

If a piece of iron were cut into four similar shaped pieces and one piece were placed in tap water, one in water from which all the air had been removed by boiling, one in dry air in a dessiccator, and one in moist air, the pieces in tap water and moist air would show rust before any appeared on the other two, indicating that both water and air are necessary for rusting to occur.

The need for air to be present is obvious in that, to form iron oxide, oxygen is required. The necessity for the moisture will become apparent after we have discussed the conduction of electricity in liquids, as rusting is a process which involves the formation of minute electrical cells on the surface of the metal, and to form a cell one must have an electrolyte (see sections 19.2, 19.5 and 24). Water acts as this electrolyte.

18.6 Damage due to rusting

As we have already mentioned, the damage due to rusting of iron and steel components costs vast sums of money. A substantial amount of this could be saved by improved design and adequate protection. Rusting cannot occur if water is not present, so the exclusion of water from the surface of a component is of prime importance. This can be achieved by painting with a water-resistant paint, by galvanizing, by plating, or by maintaining an oil or grease film on the surface, but it is important that the covering is continuous. If discontinuities occur in a film, rust will occur at these defects very rapidly.

Unfortunately, very often the parts of a metal structure that are the most susceptible to rusting, because moisture will collect there, are the hardest to cover with protective coating. If moisture gets in behind a paint film and rusting occurs, the rust will often push the paint away from the surface and allow the air to come into contact with the surface of the metal. Rust absorbs water from the atmosphere and, once rusting starts, it can build up to a dangerous level in a very short time — anyone who has experienced the short time between detecting 'blisters' where the cellulose has been pushed away from the body-work of a car to the occasion when a screwdriver can be pushed through a rusty patch will confirm this.

Damage due to rusting usually occurs first in those areas where moisture collects, and it is these areas that need constant inspection and protection. However, there is considerable scope for improvement in design and in maintenance procedures in order to reduce the extent of rusting.

Exercise G1
1. A piece of iron was weighed, then heated to 700 °C for 30 minutes in an air oven. When it was reweighed, its mass had changed. Would you expect its mass to have increased or decreased? Explain your answer. What other changes would the iron have undergone?
2. Explain what happens if a piece of paper is ignited and dropped into a jar which then has the lid screwed on. What gases would you expect to be present in the jar at the end of the experiment?
3. Discuss the steps that may be taken to reduce the likelihood of damage by corrosion to a steel component.

19 Effects of electricity on substances

Solids can be divided into good and poor conductors of electricity. The majority of the good conductors of electricity are metals. Electricity may also be conducted by liquids. We shall see that it is possible to arrange the elements in a series depending on their reactivity. Two phenomena where electrical conductivity is important — electroplating and corrosion — are discussed.

19.1 Solid conductors
One of the properties that distinguishes a metal from most non-metals is its ability to conduct electricity very easily. It is outside the scope of this book to discuss the reasons for good or poor electrical conductivity other than to say that good conductivity is due to the ability of some electrons of the substance to move freely. In Table G2, which we can use to compare the conductivity of some pure elements, the better conductors have the lower values of electrical resistivity (see sections 10.16 and 22.3).

From this table we can see that carbon is the only non-metal that has a conductivity approaching that of the metals. The other two non-metals listed, phosphorus and sulphur, have conductivities many orders of magnitude less than those of the metals.

19.2 Conduction in liquids; electroplating and cells
Figure G1 shows a circuit in which we have a strip of iron connected to the negative terminal of a battery and a strip of copper connected to the positive

Substance	Electrical resistivity ($\mu\Omega$ m)
Aluminium	2.7×10^{-2}
Carbon	70
Copper	1.7×10^{-2}
Gold	2.42×10^{-2}
Iron	9.8×10^{-2}
Lead	20.65×10^{-2}
Phosphorus	10^{21}
Silver	1.62×10^{-2}
Sulphur	1.9×10^{27}

Table G2 Electrical resistivities of some elements

terminal. The two metal strips are partly immersed in a solution of copper sulphate to which a small amount of sulphuric acid has been added. The metal strip attached to the positive terminal of the battery will acquire a positive charge and is called the *anode* or *positive electrode*; the metal attached to the negative terminal is called the *cathode* or *negative electrode*. The solution which surrounds the two electrodes is called the *electrolyte*. When this circuit is completed by closing the switch, the ammeter will show a current flowing. This means that the electrical current is flowing across the liquid between the two electrodes. When this occurs we have what is known as a *cell*. A cell consists of *two or more electrodes and an electrolyte to conduct electricity between them*.

After operating the cell in fig. G1 for a short time, it will be possible to detect two changes. The iron cathode will acquire a reddish colour and the

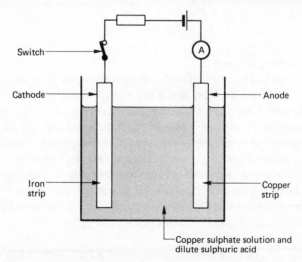

Fig. G1 A simple cell for electroplating copper

137

copper anode will become pitted and will lose mass. The reddish colour on the cathode is due to copper being deposited on its surface and the loss in mass of the anode is due to copper dissolving from its surface. In fact, if the masses of both electrodes are determined prior to connecting the circuit and redetermined some time after connection, it will be found that the cathode increases in mass by exactly the same amount as the anode decreases in mass. So copper is being transferred by some means from anode to cathode via the electrolyte. At the same time, electricity is being transferred across the electrolyte. The two transfers are related. At the anode surface, copper atoms lose two electrons, which are negative charges of electricity, and so acquire a net charge — becoming what is known as an *ion*, in this case the positively charged copper ion Cu^{++} (the two plus signs indicate how many electrons each atom has lost). This Cu^{++} ion is positively charged and so will be attracted by the negatively charged iron cathode, so it enters the electrolyte and moves across to the cathode. At the cathode, which is negatively charged, due to a concentration of electricity (which is really a stream of electrons), the Cu^{++} ion will acquire two electrons and will become a copper atom again. This copper atom is insoluble and so deposits on the surface of the iron strip.

This phenomenon is known as *electroplating*. Many metals can be deposited by electroplating. All that is required is a cell, a suitable electrolyte, an anode to act as a source of the metal to be deposited, and a supply of electricity. Electroplating, provided that the correct conditions are used, is a means whereby a very adherent compact film of one metal may be put on to the surface of another metal, either to improve its appearance (e.g. chromium plating), to improve its corrosion resistance (nickel plating), or to increase its electrical conductivity (copper plating).

19.3 Electrochemical series

We have discussed in some detail the deposition of copper from an electrolyte containing one of its salts. Most metals can be deposited from a solution containing their salts, some more easily than others, depending on the stability of the salt in solution. Some metals such as aluminium, sodium, calcium, and potassium cannot be deposited from a solution of their salts in water as the salts are too stable. They can, however, be deposited under carefully controlled conditions from a molten mixture of salts containing them. The ease with which metals can be plated out of electrolytes can be compared by using the *electrochemical series* — Table G3. This arranges metals from the most *noble* to the most *base*. Metals at the noble end of this series are more readily deposited than the base metals.

This series indicates the relative tendencies of metals to come out of solution — it does not give any information about the actual current required and the

Noble	Gold
	Silver
	Copper
	Lead
	Tin
	Nickel
	Iron
	Chromium
Base	Zinc

Table G3 Electrochemical series of some common metals

rate at which the metal may be plated out. It gives us some information also about relative tendencies of these metals to dissolve in a given solution. In general, the baser metals dissolve more readily to form an electrolyte than do the noble metals. If we were to connect a strip of copper to a strip of zinc and immerse them in a dilute acid solution, the zinc would dissolve the more readily, that is zinc atoms would be converted to zinc ions and go into solution. This means that a potential difference would be set up in the circuit, the zinc acquiring a negative charge and the copper a positive one.

In theory it should be possible to make up cells that would produce a potential difference by coupling up any two metals in an electrolyte. In general this works only for certain metals, as gas bubbles form on the surface of some metals giving rise to what is known as 'polarization'. However, the electrochemical series is a useful guide as to which metal in a bi-metal pair becomes the anode and which would dissolve first when exposed to an electrolyte.

19.4 Reactivities of metals with oxygen

The electrochemical series lists metals from the most noble to the most base and refers to their reactivities in electrolytes. The series also relates approximately to the ease with which metals form oxides, that is the ease with which they would 'scale' on exposure to the air. Gold and silver do not form oxides at room temperature — that is why they always appear bright even after prolonged exposure to the air. Metals at the other end of the series form oxides very rapidly — this is proved by the extreme stability of zinc and chromium oxides. Chromium, however, still appears bright even though it forms an oxide very easily. This is because the oxide formed on its surface is very tenacious and insulates the metal from further oxidation, so once a thin film of oxide is formed the oxidation process finishes before the surface of the chromium dulls. A full electrochemical series is very useful as a guide to whether a metal reacts readily or not so readily with oxygen, indicating whether it is safe to use the metal in construction; it also shows whether the metal may be easily extracted from its oxides — the more noble the metal, the easier it is to remove it from its oxide.

It is important to know something about the nature of the oxide film formed on the metal surface before making too many predictions about the metal's behaviour. Aluminium, which is an extremely base metal, forms an extremely protective oxide layer and in fact has a resistance to oxidation at room temperature that is greater than that of iron, which is well above it in the electrochemical series.

19.5 Electrochemical corrosion

We have already discussed in sections 18.5 and 18.6 one particular form of corrosion known as rusting. Another means whereby a great loss of strength in metals occurs is electrochemical corrosion. This occurs when designers call for metals that are widely spaced in the electrochemical series to be used in contact with each other in the presence of an electrolyte. Some designers seem to be surprised if a zinc-base die-cast trim on a steel car causes a cell to be set up and corrosion to occur when an electrolyte (e.g. impure water from the road) is present. Other designers call for a brass valve to be fitted to a steel radiator in a heating system and wonder why corrosion occurs. Copper brackets are frequently used to hold steel water pipes, and steel brackets to hold copper ones. In each of these cases we have two different metals in electrical contact in the presence of an electrolyte. We have already seen that this constitutes a cell in which electricity will flow. The more noble metal of the two becomes a cathode and the more base material becomes an anode and dissolves.

Wherever possible, if there is any chance of an electrolyte being present, the use of dissimilar metals in contact should be avoided. Where a design calls for two widely different metals to be used in an electrolyte, they should not be in electrical contact with each other — an insulating rubber or plastic gasket should be fitted.

Corrosion, like simple rusting, wastes resources, reduces the life of components and materials, and in extreme cases can be hazardous to life and limb.

Exercise G2

1. With the aid of a sketch, explain what happens if a silver rod and a copper rod are dipped into a solution of silver nitrate while the copper is connected to the negative terminal of an accumulator and the silver to the positive terminal.
2. Explain what would be likely to happen if a brass valve connected into a steel pipework system had a dilute salt solution passing through it.
3. Explain what is meant by the electrochemical series. What information can be derived from this series about (a) electroplating, (b) corrosion? What are the limitations of this information?

20 Acids, bases, and salts

In this section we will explain the difference between an acid and an alkali and describe the reactions that occur when they are mixed.

20.1 Acidity and alkalinity

The two words 'acidity' and 'alkalinity' are used to describe the properties of certain large groups of chemicals. There are many ways in which the acidity, or degree of acidness, of a chemical may be measured. One of the easiest and clearest is by the use of an *indicator*. An indicator is a naturally occurring or manufactured *chemical which has one colour in the presence of an acid substance and a different colour in the presence of an alkaline substance.* One of the most widely used acid/alkali indicators is the naturally occurring dye litmus. This gives the characteristic colour to the juice of blackberries and to beetroot. In the presence of an acid litmus is red, in the presence of an alkali it is blue.

The most convenient form of litmus for use as a quick test to decide whether a solution is acid or alkaline is litmus paper — absorbent paper that has been soaked in the dye and then allowed to dry. This can be obtained in the form of small strips which will turn blue in the presence of alkalis such as ammonium hydroxide, caustic soda (sodium hydroxide), and caustic potash (potassium hydroxide) and red in the presence of acids such as sulphuric, hydrochloric, nitric, or acetic acids. A simple demonstration of the colour changes of litmus can be made using vinegar — which contains acetic acid — which turns litmus paper red; household ammonia, which contains ammonium hydroxide, turns litmus blue.

Other indicators which are manufactured to distinguish between acids and alkalis of specific strengths include methyl orange, methyl red, and phenolphthalein. This last named has a spectacular colour change from a colourless liquid in the presence of acids to a deep wine red in the presence of alkalis.

20.2 Acids, bases, and chemical reactions

If we start with a solution that is acidic, it will have certain properties because of this acidity. It will give an acid reaction to the indicators named in the previous section; it will attack many metals and dissolve them. If we gradually add an alkali such as sodium hydroxide to this acid, the acidic properties of the solution will gradually decrease until it will no longer attack metals and eventually it will stop having the effect on indicators normally associated with an acid. This change in properties can be explained in terms of the *ions* that are present in solution. We saw in section 19.2 that ions are charged particles formed when atoms or molecules lose or gain electrons. An acid acquires its acidic properties from *hydrogen ions* (H^+) formed when the hydrogen atoms, which are present in all acids, each lose one electron.

141

So, sulphuric acid (H_2SO_4) in solution produces two hydrogen ions and a sulphate ion:

$$H_2SO_4 \rightleftharpoons 2H^+ + SO_4^{--}$$

The double arrow sign indicates a reaction which is in equilibrium, and the two negative signs after the SO_4 show that the sulphate ion has two free electrons.

Hydrochloric acid (HCl) dissociates, as this separation into ions is called, as follows:

$$HCl \rightleftharpoons H^+ + Cl^- \text{ (chloride ion)}$$

and nitric acid:

$$HNO_3 \rightleftharpoons H^+ + NO_3^- \text{ (nitrate ion)}$$

An alkali, or a soluble base, as it is frequently known, dissociates differently. If we consider sodium hydroxide (NaOH), it dissociates in the following way:

$$NaOH \rightleftharpoons Na^+ + OH^-$$

potassium hydroxide (KOH):

$$KOH \rightleftharpoons K^+ + OH^-$$

and ammonium hydroxide (NH_4OH):

$$NH_4 \rightleftharpoons NH_4^+ + OH^-$$

We can see from these reactions that they all have one thing in common — the production of the OH^- or *hydroxyl ion*

This now gives us definitions of acids and alkalis in terms of the ions produced in solutions:

an *acid* may be defined as *a substance that, in solution in water, gives rise to hydrogen ions* (H^+);

an *alkali or soluble base* is *a substance that, in solution in water, gives rise to hydroxyl ions* (OH^-).

It is interesting to note that, if water dissociates, it gives rise to both H^+ and OH^- ions:

$$H_2O \rightleftharpoons H^+ + OH^-$$

thus it may be described as neutral.

If we add an acid to a base, a *chemical reaction* will take place. A chemical reaction may be examined in stages, and it will be seen that the net effect is a rearrangement of atoms. No new atoms can be formed and no atoms can be lost — a balance must be preserved.

142

If we examine what happens when caustic soda (NaOH) is added to hydrochloric acid (HCl), we can see the stages that occur and the net result of these stages.

Stage 1: the hydrochloric acid dissociates:

$$HCl \rightleftharpoons H^+ + Cl^-$$

hydrochloric acid $\rightleftharpoons$ hydrogen ion + chloride ion

Stage 2: the sodium hydroxide dissociates:

$$NaOH \rightleftharpoons Na^+ + OH^-$$

sodium hydroxide $\rightleftharpoons$ sodium ion + hydrogen ion

Stage 3: ions of opposite sign will be attracted to each other and will combine:

$$Na^+ + Cl^- \rightleftharpoons NaCl$$

sodium ion + chloride ion $\rightleftharpoons$ sodium chloride

$$H^+ + OH^- \rightleftharpoons H_2O$$

hydrogen ion + hydroxyl ion $\rightleftharpoons$ water

The net result of these stages is

$$HCl + NaOH \rightleftharpoons NaCl + H_2O$$

hydrochloric acid + sodium hydroxide $\rightleftharpoons$ sodium chloride + water

We will consider a further example — when ammonium hydroxide is added to nitric acid, the following reaction occurs.

Stage 1: the nitric acid dissociates:

$$HNO_3 \rightleftharpoons H^+ + NO_3^-$$

nitric acid $\rightleftharpoons$ hydrogen ion + nitrate ion

Stage 2: the ammonium hydroxide dissociates:

$$NH_4OH \rightleftharpoons NH_4^+ + OH^-$$

ammonium hydroxide $\rightleftharpoons$ ammonium ion + hydroxyl ion

Stage 3: the ions of opposite signs combine:

$$NH_4^+ + NO_3^- \rightleftharpoons NH_4NO_3$$

ammonium ion + nitrate ion $\rightleftharpoons$ ammonium nitrate

$$H^+ + OH^- \rightleftharpoons H_2O$$

hydrogen ion + hydroxyl ion $\rightleftharpoons$ water

The net result of these stages is:

$$HNO_3 + NH_4OH \rightleftharpoons NH_4NO_3 + H_2O$$

nitric acid + ammonium hydroxide $\rightleftharpoons$ ammonium nitrate + water

These reactions are typical of what occurs when an acid and a base are allowed to come into contact with each other. The acid is said to be *neutralized* by the base. This means that its hydrogen ions combine with the hydroxyl ions of the base to produce water and a *salt* of the acid.

To summarize, we can say that neutralization is

ACID + BASE = SALT + WATER

Neutralization is not the only kind of chemical reaction; for example, salts which ionize in solution will change partners if one combination of ions is relatively insoluble:

sodium carbonate	+	calcium hydroxide	→	sodium hydroxide	+	calcium carbonate

potassium chromate	+	lead acetate	→	potassium acetate	+	lead chromate

Exercise G3
1. Explain the difference between the terms 'acid', 'base', 'salt'.
2. Using equations involving ions, describe the stages and the final reaction that occur when ammonium hydroxide (NH_4OH) is added to hydrochloric acid (HCl).
3. What are the stages, in ionic terms, that occur if sulphuric acid (H_2SO_4) is added to caustic soda ($NaOH$)?
4. What is meant by the term 'dissociation'? Give six examples of dissociation.

H   Rays

21 Elementary optics

The study of light and the ways in which it can be reflected and refracted is called *optics*. The path along which light energy travels is called a *ray*. A collection of rays which is emitted from a source of light is called a *beam*. The behaviour of light rays is usually studied by generating thin rays of light in a *ray box* which contains a lamp and emits rays through a narrow slit.

Light always travels in straight lines, although the direction of these straight lines can be changed by reflection and refraction, which will be discussed in the following sections.

21.1 Reflection of light by a plane mirror

If a thin ray of light is allowed to strike a plane mirror as shown in fig. H1, the ray IO which travels towards the mirror is called the *incident ray* and makes an angle i with a line NO which is drawn at right angles to the mirror at the point O where the ray strikes the mirror. Angle i is called the *angle of incidence*. NO is called the *normal* at the point of incidence. The *reflected ray* OR traces the path of the light ray after it has been reflected from the mirror. The angle r is called the *angle of reflection*.

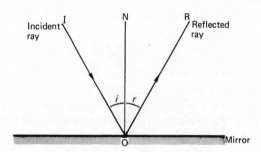

Fig. H1 Reflection from a plane mirror

It will always be found that $i = r$, regardless of their values. This is the first law of reflection at a plane surface, namely

the angle of incidence is always equal to the angle of reflection.

In the case we have illustrated in fig. H1, the incident ray, the reflected ray, and the normal at the point of incidence all lie in the same plane, that is the plane represented by the paper. This is always the case regardless of the plane. This is the second law of reflection:

the incident ray, the reflected ray, and the normal are always in the same plane

21.2 Ray paths at plane mirrors

The paths of rays which strike plane mirrors can be illustrated by the simple periscope, fig. H2, which shows how a ray of light from A strikes a plane mirror at an angle of 45° at B. As $i = r = 45°$, $A\hat{B}C = 90°$, so the ray is turned through 90°. If it then meets another mirror at 45° at a point C, $p = q = 45°$, so $B\hat{C}D = 90°$ and the ray is turned through 90° again. As the two mirrors are

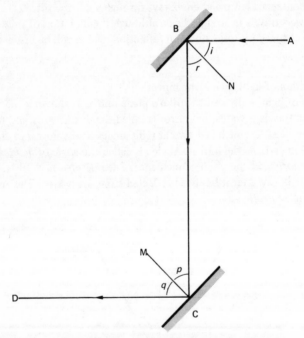

Fig. H2 Principle of the periscope, showing the path of a light ray

parallel, the light rays stay in the same plane; what happens is that the light from A ends up travelling in a direction parallel to its original direction but displaced downwards by the distance apart of the two parallel mirrors, BC.

Figure H3 shows how the laws of reflection might be used to arrange four mirrors a, b, c, d so that light could be made to travel around a solid object such as a house brick. To an observer looking downwards at E, light travelling

146

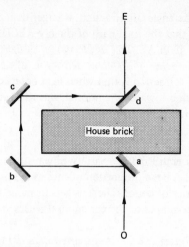

Fig. H3 How to see 'through' a solid object

from O will be diverted round the brick but will eventually, after reflection at d, revert to a path in line with its original path and appear to come from point O.

21.3 The path of light rays passing through a parallel-sided glass block

We have seen what happens to a light ray when it meets a reflecting surface, such as a plane mirror. It behaves differently when it falls upon a substance through which it can pass. Figure H4 shows a ray of light starting at A which enters a rectangular glass prism at B. If NM is the normal at B and i is the angle of incidence, we find that the path of the ray changes so that it moves towards the normal; that is angle r, *the angle of refraction*, is smaller than i. If C is the point at which the ray leaves the prism and RS is the normal at this point, we find that as the ray leaves the block its direction changes so that it moves away

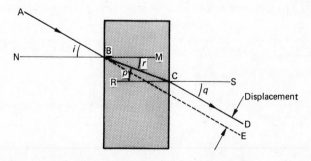

Fig. H4 Path of a light ray through a rectangular glass prism

147

from the normal: q, the angle of refraction, is larger than p, the angle of incidence. We can see that the final path of the ray ABCD is displaced from but parallel to the original path AE. This *displacement of light rays as they pass from one medium to another of different density* is called *refraction*.

The general rule of refraction is that when light enters a dense medium from a less dense it is refracted towards the normal, and when it passes from a dense to a less dense medium it is refracted away from normal

21.4 Lenses

The refraction of light is utilized in a variety of ways that may be of considerable scientific benefit. A large proportion of these ways involve light passing through a lens or a series of lenses. The lens gets its name from the Latin word for a bean, because the shapes of the commonest lenses are similar to those of beans or lentils.

A *lens* is a *piece of glass or other transparent material whose thickness varies from the middle to the edges, bounded by spherical surfaces on one or both sides.*

Since very early times, lenses have been used to bring together rays of light in a concentrated form. They were originally known as 'burning glasses' because the sun's rays could be concentrated to such an extent that sufficient heat could be generated to start a fire.

Lenses are used in spectacles to improve vision, in microscopes to make very small objects easily visible, in telescopes to make distance objects appear near, and in cameras and projectors to produce a sharp image on a film or a screen.

There are a large number of different shaped lenses in common use, but for convenience they may be grouped under two headings — converging or diverging lenses. *Converging lenses* cause rays of light to come together after passing through them, and *diverging lenses* cause rays of light to spread out after passing through them.

Figure H5 shows examples of each of these types of lens. (a) is what is known as a bi-convex lens, because both of its surfaces curve outwards. The surfaces can have the same or different radii of curvature, depending on the use of the lens. (b) is known as a bi-concave lens, having both of its surfaces curving

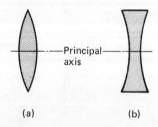

Fig. H5 (a) Bi-convex lens (b) Bi-concave lens

148

inwards. Again the radii of curvature can be the same or different in a bi-concave lens. (a) is an example of a converging lens and (b) is an example of a diverging lens. The line passing through the centres of curvature of the lens surfaces is known as the *principal axis* of the lens.

21.5 Rays passing through a lens
In order to study the paths of rays of light passing through lenses, a ray box is needed with a series of slits which emit parallel rays of light. If several of these rays of light are allowed to pass through a bi-convex lens, they will be seen to converge at a point F, fig. H6(a). This point F is called a *focus* or a *focal point* of the lens.

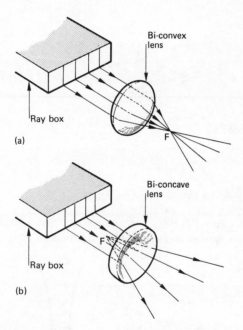

Fig. H6 Focal points of lenses

If parallel rays of light pass through a biconcave lens, fig. H6(b), they will diverge so that they all appear to come from a point F which is between the source of light and the lens. This point is a *focal point* of the lens.

For rays of light parallel to the principal axis of a converging or diverging lens, the focal point will be on the principal axis and is known as the *principal focus* of the lens. The principal focus is defined as *the point through which all rays of light parallel to the principal axis pass when they emerge from a con-*

149

verging lens, or the point from which they all appear to come when they emerge from a diverging lens.

The distance from the principal focus to the optical centre of a lens is called the *focal length* of that lens.

21.6 Virtual and real images

Figure H7 illustrates how an eye collects rays from an object (such as an illuminated bulb) after reflection from a plane mirror. To the eye, the rays appear to come from a point behind the mirror and the diagram shows how the eye sees what seems to be an image of the bulb as far behind the mirror as the object is in front. There is nothing actually behind the mirror — no real image and no real rays — so such an image is called a *virtual* image.

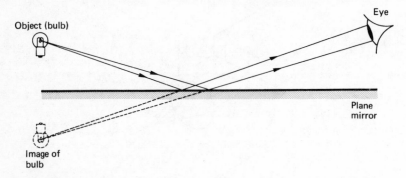

Fig. H7 Formation of a virtual image by a mirror

With a *concave* lens, fig. H8, the image is always virtual, upright, and smaller than the object, however far the object is from the lens.

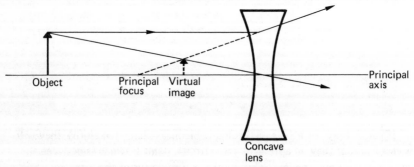

Fig. H8 Formation of a virtual image by a concave lens

With a *convex* lens, fig. H9, the image is virtual, upright, and enlarged if the distance of the object from the lens is less than the focal length of the lens. In this case, the convex lens acts as a magnifying glass.

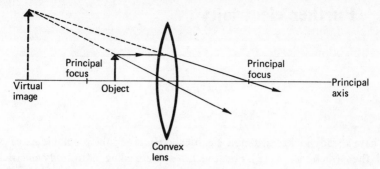

Fig. H9 Formation of a virtual image by a convex lens

If the object is beyond the focal length of the convex lens, fig. H10, the image is inverted and it can be projected on to a screen, i.e. it is a *real* image. The image is the same size as the object when the image and the object are the same distance from the lens; otherwise, whichever is closer to the lens is smaller than the other.

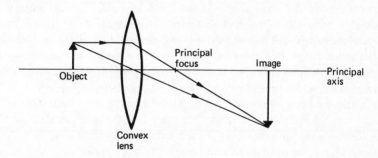

Fig. H10 Formation of a real image by a convex lens

Exercise H1
1. State the laws of reflection of light. With the aid of sketches, show how it is possible to use mirrors to see over a 2 m high wall.
2. What are the differences between converging and diverging lenses? What are the uses of each of these types of lens?
3. Draw a diagram to show the path of a light ray which strikes a rectangular glass block at an angle of 80°. Name all the angles and rays.

151

I   Further electricity

We have already looked at simple electrical circuits and the problems associated with them (sections 10–13). For students who are going on to study electricity in more detail, this section deals with some more important principles.

22 More about resistance

22.1 Temperature coefficient of resistance
We have already seen in section 10.17 that the resistance of a material changes with temperature. In the example quoted we said that the resistance of a certain length of copper wire was 1 Ω at 0 °C and 1.426 Ω at 100 °C. If the increase is assumed to be regular over the whole temperature range it is clear that a rise in temperature of 1 °C will produce a rise in resistance of 0.426/100 = 0.004 26 Ω.

The value, 0.004 26/°C, is called the *temperature coefficient of resistance* of copper and is defined as *the increase in resistance per unit resistance per °C rise in temperature* and is usually indicated by the Greek letter α ('*alpha*').

If a material has a resistance R_1 at θ_1 °C and a temperature coefficient of resistance α, the increase of resistance for every 1 °C rise in temperature will be $R_1\alpha$. If the temperature rises to θ_2 °C, the increase in resistance will be $R_1\alpha(\theta_2 - \theta_1)$. If the resistance at temperature θ_2 is R_2, then

$$R_2 = \text{resistance at } \theta_1 \text{ °C + increase in resistance}$$

$$= R_1 + R_1\alpha(\theta_2 - \theta_1)$$

$$R_2 = R_1[1 + \alpha(\theta_2 - \theta_1)]$$

22.2 Problems involving the temperature coefficient of resistance
In order to make the principles discussed in section 22.1 more clear, we shall look at some calculations.

Example 1   A 1 m length of aluminium rod has a resistance of 30 Ω at 25 °C. What is its resistance at 65 °C? The temperature coefficient of resistance of aluminium is 0.004 02/°C.

$$R_{65} = R_{25}[1 + 0.004\,02\,(65 - 25)]$$

$$= 30\ \Omega(1 + 0.1608)$$

$$= 34.824 \ \Omega$$

i.e. at 65 °C the resistance is 34.824 Ω.

Example 2 The resistance of a coil of copper wire at 15 °C is 180 Ω. After a current has passed for several hours, the resistance rises to 214 Ω. Calculate the temperature to which the coil has risen. (α for copper is 0.004 26/°C.)

Let the new temperature = θ °C

$$214 \ \Omega = 180 \ \Omega [1 + 0.004\,26(\theta - 15)]$$

$$214 = 180 + [180 \times 0.004\,26(\theta - 15)]$$

$$\theta - 15 = \frac{214 - 180}{180 \times 0.004\,26}$$

$$= \frac{34}{0.7668} = 44.34$$

∴ $$\theta = 44.34 + 15 = 59.34$$

i.e. the temperature of the coil rises to 59.34 °C.

22.3 Resistivity
We have seen in section 10.16 that the resistance of a conductor depends on its length, its cross-sectional area, and the material from which it is made. These quantities are related by the expression

$$R = \rho \frac{l}{a}$$

where l = length, a = cross-sectional area, and ρ = a constant. The constant ρ is known as the *resistivity*. The resistivity of a material may be defined as the resistance of a piece of that material 1 m long and 1 m^2 in cross-sectional area. It can be expressed in ohm metres (Ω m) but because this gives very low values it is normally expressed in microhm metres ($\mu\Omega$ m).

22.4 Problems involving resistivity

Example 1 Calculate the cross-sectional area of a piece of copper wire 31.2 m long that has a resistance of 0.3 Ω. (Resistivity of copper = 0.017 $\mu\Omega$ m.)

$$R = \rho \frac{l}{a}$$

$$0.3 \ \Omega = 0.017 \times 10^{-6} \ \Omega \, \text{m} \times \frac{31.2 \ \text{m}}{a}$$

$$a = \frac{31.2 \text{ m} \times 0.017 \times 10^{-6} \ \Omega \text{m}}{0.3 \ \Omega}$$

$$= 1.766 \times 10^{-6} \text{ m}^2$$

$$= 1.766 \text{ mm}^2$$

i.e. the cross-sectional area of the wire is 1.766 mm^2.

Example 2 Calculate the resistance of 1 km of overhead power cable made of aluminium if the diameter of the cable is 10 mm. (Resistivity of aluminium = $0.028 \ \mu\Omega$ m.)

$$R = \rho \ \frac{l}{a}$$

$$= \frac{0.028 \times 10^{-6} \ \Omega \text{m} \times 10^3 \text{ m}}{\pi \times (5 \times 10^{-3} \text{ m})^2}$$

$$= 0.36 \ \Omega$$

i.e. the resistance of the cable is $0.36 \ \Omega$.

22.5 Conductors and insulators

We have seen that, for electricity to flow in a circuit, the circuit has to be continuous. If there is a break — an air gap for example — the electricity ceases to flow. Air prevents the flow of electricity and is called an *insulator*. The materials through which the electricity flows are called *conductors*.

Examples of insulators are air, plastic, rubber, wood, cork, pure water.

Examples of conductors are metals and solutions of salts or acids.

We have seen some values of the resistivity of elements in section 19.1; the resistivities of some other materials at normal temperatures are given in Table I1.

Substance	Resistivity ($\mu\Omega$ m)
Ebonite	10^{20}
Glass	10^{15}
Mica	10^{19}
Oil	10^{17}
Paper (dry)	10^{16}
Porcelain	10^{16}
p.v.c.	10^{21}
Rubber	10^{22}

Table I1 Typical values of resistivity

Exercise I1

1. The resistance of 100 m of wire of 0.12 mm diameter is 1200 Ω. Calculate the resistivity of the wire material.

2. Calculate the resistance of 1 km of aluminium wire with a diameter of 3 mm. The resistivity of aluminium is 0.028 $\mu\Omega$ m.

3. An electric motor has a coil which is composed of copper wire which has a resistance of 120 Ω at 0 °C. What would its resistance be if, when it is running, its temperature rises to 50 °C? Assume the temperature coefficient of resistance of copper is 0.0043/°C.

4. An aluminium cable is 2 km long and has a diameter of 10 mm. Calculate its resistance at 60 °C if the resistivity of aluminium at 20 °C is 0.03 $\mu\Omega$ m and its temperature coefficient of resistance is 0.004/°C.

23 E.M.F. and internal resistance

We have already discussed the meaning of potential difference and voltage (section 10.3) and how they are measured across two points in a circuit (section 10.4). The idea of electromotive force (e.m.f.) will be discussed in this section and we shall see how it relates to potential difference.

23.1 Electromotive force
The electromotive force (e.m.f.) of a cell is the maximum potential difference that can be produced by the cell to drive an electric current round a circuit. The potential difference across the terminals of a cell depends on how much current is being produced by the cell — it decreases as the amount of current, or the 'load' on the cell, increases. If the potential difference across the terminals is measured when virtually no current is being produced, or under *no load*, it will correspond to the e.m.f. of the cell.

23.2 Measurement of e.m.f.
We have said in the previous section that to measure the e.m.f. of a cell we need to measure the potential difference across the terminals when the minimum amount of current is being withdrawn. This is achieved by connecting across the terminals a voltmeter which has an extremely high resistance. Under these circumstances, very little current flows in the measuring circuit.

If we need to measure the e.m.f. of a battery of several cells, they must be connected in series with the positive terminal of one cell connected to the negative terminal of the next, and the high-resistance voltmeter connected in series with all of the cells.

23.3 Internal resistance

The reason for the difference in potential across the terminals of a cell when it is under 'no-load' conditions and when it is 'on circuit' (i.e. when it is giving out a current) can be explained as follows. If the e. m. f. of a cell is measured as described in the preceding section and it is, for example, 1.5 V, it could be that when a current flows in the external circuit its potential difference falls to 0.9 V. This value of 0.9 V corresponds to the potential difference in the circuit outside the cell and, if the current flowing is found to be 0.3 A, then the *external resistance* of the circuit is given by Ohm's law as

$$R = \frac{V}{I} = \frac{0.9 \text{ V}}{0.3 \text{ A}} = 3 \ \Omega$$

Since the e.m.f. of the cell is 1.5 V, and 0.9 V are used to maintain a current through the external resistance, 1.5 V − 0.9 V = 0.6 V must be used to maintain the current through the *internal resistance* of the cell. The internal resistance is *the resistance due to the chemicals inside the cell.*

The internal resistance can be calculated from Ohm's law to be:

$$r = \frac{V}{I} = \frac{0.6 \text{ V}}{0.3 \text{ A}} = 2 \ \Omega$$

24 Primary and secondary cells

Electricity can be stored in cells. There are two basic classes of cell — primary and secondary cells. Each class contains a large number of different types of cell. The cells differ because they contain different electrolytes to conduct the electricity inside them. The materials from which the plates in the cells are made can also differ widely.

24.1 The difference between primary and secondary cells

The principal property of primary cells, such as the Leclanché cell (fig. I1), that distinguishes them from secondary cells such as the lead—acid cell (fig. I2) is that the chemicals in them are gradually used up and the chemical reactions that occur are not reversible. Eventually all the chemicals are exhausted and the cell becomes useless. Secondary cells may be recharged by applying a potential across them that reverses the chemical reactions that occur when they give off a current. They can therefore be used for long periods, as long as they are periodically recharged, whereas a primary cell, once exhausted, has to be scrapped.

24.2 Lead—acid cell

A lead—acid cell (fig. I2) is composed of a series of positive plates, which are made of lead peroxide held in a grid of lead—antimony alloy, and negative plates which are usually pure lead held in a similar grid. These plates are separated by insulators and are surrounded by an electrolyte of dilute sulphuric acid.

156

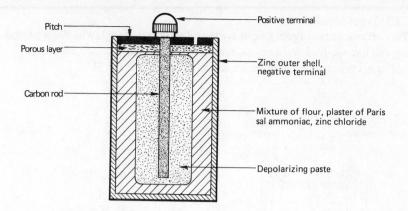

Fig. I1 Leclanché cell

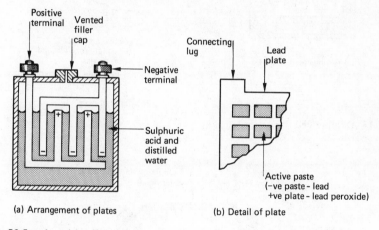

(a) Arrangement of plates   (b) Detail of plate

Fig. I2 Lead–acid cell

When the cell gives off electricity it is said to be discharging, and the plates become coated with lead sulphate while the relative density of the electrolyte decreases.

When the cell is connected to a battery charger, the lead sulphate on the positive and negative plates is converted back to lead peroxide and lead respectively and the relative density of the acid rises.

The relative density of the electrolyte may be measured and used as a guide to the state of charge of the cell — the electrolyte in a fully charged cell usually has a relative density of 1.25.

24.3 Types of cell

Two other common types of cell are the alkaline cell, fig. I3, which is a secondary cell like the lead—acid cell shown in fig. I2, and the mercury cell, fig. I4, which is a primary cell like the Leclanché cell shown in fig. I1.

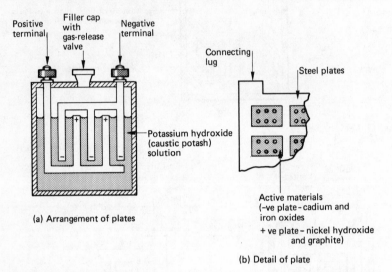

(a) Arrangement of plates

(b) Detail of plate

Fig. I3 Alkaline cell

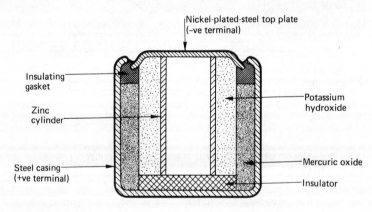

Fig. I4 Mercury cell

Revision exercises

1. What is the mass of a cube of lead (density 11.37×10^3 kg/m^3 if its sides are 24 mm long?
2. What is the width of a rectangular block of steel (density 7.8×10^3 kg/m^3) if it is 15 mm long, 10 mm high, and has a mass of 23.7 g?
3. Which has the greater mass: 2 m of round copper bar or 2.5 m of round iron bar? The diameters of both bars are equal and their densities are in the ratio 8:7.
4. An irregular piece of metal has a mass of 7.25 g. When it is placed in a beaker of water filled to the brim it causes 1.2 g of water to overflow. What is the density of the metal?
5. A piece of iron 500 mm long × 200 mm wide and 20 mm thick has an internal cavity. If the iron has a mass of 14.6 kg and the density of iron is 7.8×10^3 kg/m^3, calculate the volume of the cavity.
6. A piece of steel pipe is 4 m long and has a mass of 275 kg. The external diameter of the pipe is 160 mm. What is the thickness of the pipe?
   (Density of steel = 7.8×10^3 kg/m^3.)
7. (a) What is the volume of a cylindrical tank 2.5 m deep with a diameter of 1 m?
   (b) How many litres of water will it hold when it is filled to a depth of 2.25 m?
8. An alloy rod is 6 m long with a cross-sectional area of 1250 mm^2 and has a load of 10 kN applied to one end. By how much will it extend if E for the alloy is 6×10^{10} N/m^2?
9. What is the maximum pull that can be withstood by a tie-rod of 50 mm diameter if the stress is limited to 150 N/mm^2?
10. What is the maximum pull that can be applied to a copper wire 20 m long and 8 mm in diameter if it must not extend by more than 2 mm? E = 110 000 N/mm^2.
11. What is the difference between an element and a compound? Give five examples of each that can be found in the home.
12. What is (a) the difference and (b) the relationship between the atomic number and the relative atomic mass of an element?
13. Give five examples of (a) suspensions (b) solutions that can be found in everyday use.
14. How would you decide whether a material was crystalline or amorphous? Give three examples of each of these types of material.
15. A metal rod of original length 100 mm is stretched by applying a gradually increasing load. When the length of the rod was measured under different loads the following results were obtained:

Load (kN)	0	20	40	60	70	75	80
Length (mm)	100	100.15	100.30	100.45	100.58	100.75	101.20

    Calculate the work done in extending the load by (a) 0.5 mm, (b) 1.0 mm.
16. A spring contracts from 200 mm long to 50 mm long as the force stretching it is uniformly reduced from 1.5 kN to zero. Draw the resulting work diagram and determine the total work done.
17. An overhead crane lifts a mass of 100 kg through a height of 3 m when 7.84 kJ of energy are supplied to it. Calculate the efficiency of the crane.

18. In question 17, calculate the power required if the lifting takes 5 seconds.
19. To what height will a mass of 100 kg be lifted in 30 seconds by a process that uses 0.5 kW?
20. Explain why a pan containing 200 g of water takes longer to reach boiling point than the same pan with 100 g of water in it under the same conditions.
21. Draw a mercury-in-glass thermometer and discuss its important features.
22. Draw the graph of temperature against time that you would expect to result if heat were continuously and uniformly supplied to a block of ice in a container. Explain the shape of the graph.
23. How much heat is given off when 5 kg of paraffin cool from 30 °C to 5 °C?
24. A block of ice of mass 1 kg at −10 °C has heat supplied to it until it melts. The resulting water is then heated until half of it has boiled away. How much heat is required.
25. Heat can be transferred by (a) conduction, (b) convection, (c) radiation. List four examples of each.
26. Explain why a vacuum flask may be used to prevent ice cream from melting or to keep soup hot.
27. The coefficient of linear expansion of a metal rod is $14 \times 10^{-6}/$ °C. To what temperature must a rod of this metal be heated from 20 °C so that it extends from 3.25 m to 3.30 m?
28. List all the examples of wave motion that you have encountered in everyday life.
29. Explain with the help of a sketch the meaning of the terms in the expression $v = f \lambda$.
30. State Ohm's law and use it to calculate the resistances in circuits where the potential differences and currents are as follows: (a) 10 V, 2 A; (b) 100 mV, 0.1 A; (c) 1 kV, 0.5 μA; (d) 1 V, 8 mA; (e) 7 V, 1.4 μA; (f) 10 V, 5 kA.
31. Calculate the value of the resistance of two resistors, one of which has half the resistance of the other, if they are connected in parallel with a potential source of 100 V and they allow a current of 1 mA to flow. What current would flow if these same two resistors were connected in series with the same potential source?
32. Give two examples of each of the three effects that can be produced when an electric current flows.
33 Calculate the power consumed by a circuit which has three resistors, each of 10 MΩ, connected in parallel with a 250 V source.
34. A train travels at 100 km/h for 1 h, and 50 km/h for the next ½ h. If it travels at 75 km/h for the remainder of its journey, how long will it take to cover 200 km? What is its average speed?
35. A train sets of from Kettering and travels towards London at an average speed of 80 km/h at the same time as a train leaves London and travels towards Kettering at an average speed of 120 km/h. If the distance between London and Kettering is 120 km, how far will the trains be from London when they meet?
36. A bus is travelling at 10 m/s when it brakes. If it covers 15 m before it stops, calculate (a) its speed after 1 second braking time, (b) its total braking time.
37. Explain the following:
(a) it requires less force to pull a sledge across a frozen lake than on a gravel path;
(b) it is easier to slide a mass of 50 g across a wooden bench than a mass of 500 g of the same material;
(c) oil is not a good thing to have on brake linings;
(d) brake discs become hot when the brakes are applied.
38. What is the difference between a scalar and a vector quantity? Give examples of each.
39. A level-crossing barrier is 6 m long and is pivoted on a horizontal axis at a point 1 m

from one end. If the barrier has a total mass of 84 kg, calculate the mass that has to suspended on its end to balance it in a horizontal position.

40. Describe, with sketches, two methods of measuring the pressure of a gas.
41. Which areas on the bodywork of a car are most likely to be damaged by rusting? Give reasons.
42. List five examples in your college or your place of work where electrochemical corrosion is likely to occur.
43. Explain the meaning of the following terms: (a) electrolyte, (b) electrochemical series, (c) electroplating, (d) electrochemical corrosion, (e) electrolytic machining.
44. Give chemical equations for reactions between iron and oxygen, sodium and chlorine, caustic soda and hydrochloric acid, and ammonium hydroxide and nitric acid.
45. Using ray diagrams to illustrate your answer, distinguish between the terms (a) reflection and refraction, (b) concave and convex, (c) converging and diverging.
46. Explain the difference between the terms resistance and resistivity.
47. Calculate the resistivity of a copper alloy if a wire 30 m long with a cross-sectional area of 1.8 mm^2 has a resistance of 0.3 Ω.
48. What are the differences between primary and secondary cells? Sketch and label one example of each.
49. What materials would you use to manufacture the following: (a) roof insulating material? (b) power cable? (c) kettles? (d) car bodies? (e) exhaust pipes for cars? (f) brake linings? Give your reasons.
50. What were each of the following famous for? (a) Lord Kelvin, (b) Volta, (c) Hertz, (d) Young, (e) Joule, (f) Pascal, (g) Leucippus.

Answers to numerical exercises

Exercise A1
1. (a) 9.1 m², (b) 31.3 m
2. 3750 kg
3. (a) 2 m, (b) 2.53 litres
4. (a) 890 kg/m³, (b) 14.3 kg
5. 39.4 kg
6. Copper (2.8 m), steel (2.56 m), aluminium (1.05 m)
7. 760 kg/m³

Exercise A2
1. 3.27 N/mm²
2. 3 N
3. 300 kN
4. 200 000 N/mm²
5. (a) 500 N/mm², (b) 3.33×10^{-3}, (c) 1.67 mm
6. 10 mm²
7. (a) 1.96 N/mm², (b) 0.08 mm
8. 17.6 kN

Exercise A3
5. 3.79×10^{22}

Exercise B1
1. 34.34 kJ
2. 30 kg
3. 125 J
4. 98.1 kJ
5. (a) 146 kJ, (b) 111 kJ

Exercise B2
3. (a) 40 N, (b) 400 W
4. 27.5 m
5. (a) 25.5 kg, (b) 5 kJ
6. (a) 9.17 m, (b) 500 W
7. 3.06 m
8. 12.7%, 4.12 kW
9. (a) 400 MJ, (b) 667 W

Exercise B3
4. (a) −16.9 °C, (b) 205 °C, (c) 11.3 °C

Exercise B4
1. 8380 kJ
2. 195 kJ
3. 1.1°C
4. 780 kg
5. 462 °C
6. 21.3 °C
7. 49.5 kg
8. 6.21 kg
9. 4.59 kg
10. 28.4 °C

Exercise B5
1. 4.4 MJ
2. 39.4 °C
3. 22.6 MJ
4. 2.72 kg
5. 809 g
6. 1.59 kg, 8.41 kg
7. 1.71 s
8. 9.4 °C

Exercise B7
1. 1×10^{-5} /°C
2. 0.9 mm
3. 104 mm
4. 33 m

Exercise C1
1. 3.1 m
3. 3.39×10^8 m/s
4. 6.8 km

Exercise D1
1. 30 kΩ
2. 975 Ω
3. 50 MΩ
4. 84.4 V
5. 20 Ω
6. (a) 2.49 A, (b) 1.2 A
7. 0.75 Ω

Exercise D2
1. 12 A
2. 100 μW
3. 417 Ω
4. (a) 1.8 A, 21.6 W, (b) 1.2 A,
   14.4 W; 0.6A, 7.2 W
5. 600 μW
6. 115 Ω

Exercise E1
1. (a) 6.3 km/h, (b) 15.8 km,
   (c) 76.2 min
2. (a) 6 s, (b) 16.7 m
3. (a) 8 m/s, (b) 28.8 km/h, (c) 10 s
4. (a) 85 km, (b) 56.7 km/h
5. (a) 18.8 km/h, (b) 18.8 km/h
6. (a) 0.6 m/s, (b) 3.28 m/s
   (c) 3.4 m/s

Exercise E2
1. (a) 15 km/h, (b) 40 min
2. 42.4 km/h
3. 24 min
4. (a) 34.8 km/h, (b) 81 min
5. (a) 1.25 m/s^2, (b) 160 m
6. (a) 20 s (b), 4 s
7. (a) 5.56 m/s^2, (b) 333 m/s,
   (c) 1h
8. (a) 29.4 m/s, (b) 44.1 m
9. (a) 44.1 m, (b) 1.5 s, 4.5 s
10. (a) 1.91 m/s^2, (b) 13.1 s

Exercise E3
1. (a) 0.132, (b) 910 N
2. (a) 44.1 kN, (b) 4410 kJ
   (c) 2.45 kW
3. (a) 1 kg, (b) 0.255
4. (a) 3.5 kN, (b) 7.78 tonnes

Exercise F1
2. 1.25 kg
3. (a) 75 N downward
   (b) 175 N upward
4. 29.4 N
5. 392.4 N, 1570 N
6. 2.35 kN, 9.42 kN
7. 420 N, 561 N
8. 7 N
9. East
10. 90°

Exercise F2
1. (a) 6.25 MN/m^2 (b) 156 kN/m^2
2. 20.4 m
3. 227 mm
4. 2.04 m

Exercise I1
1. 0.136 μΩ m
2. 3.96 Ω
3. 146 Ω
4. 7.76 Ω

163

Index

absolute pressure, 131–2
acceleration, 104–11
    of falling body, 107–8
    due to gravity, 3, 10, 107–8
    negative, 104, 106
acid, 141–4
air, composition, 133
air resistance, 107
alcohol thermometer, 43
alkali, 141, 142
alkaline cell, 158
alloy, 28
alternating current, 94–5
ammeter, 74–5
amorphous solids, 22
ampere, 73
Ampère, A. M., 73
angle
    of incidence, 145
    of reflection, 145
    of refraction, 147
angular velocity, 111–12
anode, 137, 139
Archimedes, 4
armature, 92
atmospheric pressure, 44, 129–30,
        131–2
atom, 15–17
    structure, 17
atomic number, 17
average speed, 96, 100–3

bar, 128
base, 142, 144
base metals, 138–40
beam
    of light, 145
    supported, 122–5
    reactions, 122–5
bi-concave lens, 148–9, 150
bi-convex lens, 148–9, 150–1
bimetal strip, 64–5
Black, Joseph, 50
body-centred cubic structure, 26
Bourdon gauge, 132
brittle materials, 14

brush, carbon, 92, 95
burning, 134

cathode, 137
cell, 135, 137, 156–8
    alkaline, 158
    lead–acid, 156–7
    Leclanché, 156–7
    mercury, 158
    primary, 156, 158
    secondary, 156–8
Celsius, Anders, 42
Celsius scale, 42–3
centre of gravity, 124–6
charge, electrical, 73
chemical effect of an electric current, 87
chemical energy, 35
chemical equations, 18–19
chemical reactions, 133–44
circuits, electric, 73–84
close-packed hexagonal structure, 26
coefficient
    of cubic expansion, 64
    of friction, 114–16
    of linear expansion, 63
    of resistance, temperature, 152–3
columnar crystals, 26
columnar grains, 26
combustion, 134
commutator, 92–3
compound, 17–18
compression, 10–11
concave lens, 148–9, 150
conduction
    electrical, in liquids, 136–7
    of heat, 58, 59–61, 62
conductivity, electrical, 136
conductors
    electrical, 85, 154
        current-carrying, force on, 91
        magnetic field of, 90
    of heat, 60–1, 62
conservation of energy, 35
convection, 58–9, 61, 62
converging lens, 148–9, 150–1
conversion of energy, 35–6, 38–9, 116

164

165

166

parallel connection, 75, 78, 81–4, 85
pascal, 12, 128
Pascal, Blaise, 12, 128
periscope, 146
plastic behaviour, 14
polarization, 139
polycrystalline structure, 27
potential difference, 74–84
   and current, 75–7
   measurement of, 75
   across parallel circuit, 82
   in series circuit, 79
power, 37–9
   electrical, 38–9, 87–9
prefixes for units, 2
pressure, 128–32
   absolute, 131–2
   atmospheric, 44, 129–30, 131–2
   gauge, 131–2
   measurement, 130–2
principal axis, 148
principal focus, 148–9
principle of moments, 120–5
proton, 17

radian, 111
radiation of heat, 59, 62
radius of lens, 148–9
ray, 145
   box, 145
reaction
   beam supports, 122–5
   chemical, 133–44
   normal, 113, 114
real image, 150–1
Réamur scale, 42
recrystallization, 27
reflection, 70, 144–7
   angle of, 145
   laws of, 145–6
refraction, 70, 148
   angle of, 147
   law of, 148
relative atomic mass, 16
relative density, 8–9
   of electrolyte in cell, 157
resistance (*see also* resistors), 76, 152–4
   internal, 156
   of meters, 75
   variation with temperature, 76, 85, 152–3
resistivity, 85, 153–4
   tables of, 137, 154
resistors
   in parallel, 82–4
   in series, 79–81

symbol, 74
resultant of coplanar forces, 126–7
rotation, speed of, 111
rusting, 135–6

salt, 144
saturated solution, 22
scalar quantities, 104, 118
scale of vector, 119
sense of force, 118
sensible heat, 50–1
series connection, 75, 78–81, 85
shear, 10–11
SI units, 1
   of area, 1
   of current, 73
   of energy, 45
   of force, 3
   of frequency, 68
   of length, 1
   of mass, 3
   of potential difference, 74
   of power, 37
   prefixes for, 2
   of resistance, 77
   of stress, 12
   of temperature, 43
   of volume, 1
   of work, 30
slip-ring, 95
slope of speed–time graph, 106–7
solenoid, 90–1
solid solution, 28
solubility, 20–1
solute, 19
solution, 19–22
   saturated, 22
   solid, 28
solvent, 19
sound
   energy, 39, 70–1
   generation, 72
   waves, 71–2
south pole of magnet, 90
space lattice, 25
specific heat capacity, 45–9, 54–7
   table of, 46
specific latent heat, 53–7
   of fusion, 53
   of vapourization, 53
speed, 96, 104
   average, 96, 100–3
   of rotation, 111
speed–time graphs, 105–8
   slope of, 106–7
spring, work done in extending, 32–3